Engineering and Construction Subcontract

This contract should be used for the appointment of a subcontractor for engineering and construction work where the contractor has been appointed under the NEC3 Engineering and Construction Contract

An NEC document

April 2013

Construction Clients' Board endorsement of NEC3

The Construction Clients' Board recommends that public sector organisations use the NEC3 contracts when procuring construction. Standardising use of this comprehensive suite of contracts should help to deliver efficiencies across the public sector and promote behaviours in line with the principles of *Achieving Excellence in Construction*.

Cabinet Office UK

NEC is a division of Thomas Telford Ltd, which is a wholly owned subsidiary of the Institution of Civil Engineers (ICE), the owner and developer of the NEC.

The NEC is a family of standard contracts, each of which has these characteristics:

- Its use stimulates good management of the relationship between the two parties to the contract and, hence, of the work included in the contract.
- It can be used in a wide variety of commercial situations, for a wide variety of types of work and in any location.
- It is a clear and simple document – using language and a structure which are straightforward and easily understood.

NEC3 Engineering and Construction Subcontract is one of the NEC family and is consistent with all other NEC3 documents.

ISBN (complete box set) 978 0 7277 5867 5
ISBN (this document) 978 0 7277 5881 1

Consultative edition 1991
First edition 1993
Second edition November 1995
Third edition June 2005
Reprinted with amendments 2007
Reprinted 2008, 2009, 2010, 2012
Reprinted with amendments 2013
Reprinted 2015

British Library Cataloguing in Publication Data for this publication is available from the British Library.

Typeset by Academic + Technical, Bristol

Printed and bound in Great Britain by Bell & Bain Limited, Glasgow, UK

CONTENTS

Foreword			v
Preface			vii
Acknowledgements			ix
Amendments			x
Schedule of Options			1
Core clauses	1	General	3
	2	The *Subcontractor*'s main responsibilities	7
	3	Time	9
	4	Testing and Defects	11
	5	Payment	13
	6	Compensation events	15
	7	Title	20
	8	Risks and insurance	21
	9	Termination	24
Main Option clauses	A	Priced subcontract with activity schedule	27
	B	Priced subcontract with bill of quantities	29
	C	Target subcontract with activity schedule	31
	D	Target subcontract with bill of quantities	34
	E	Cost reimbursable subcontract	38
Dispute resolution	W1	Option W1	40
	W2	Option W2	43
Secondary Option clauses	X1	Price adjustment for inflation	46
	X2	Changes in the law	47
	X3	Multiple currencies	47
	X4	Parent company guarantee	47
	X5	Sectional Completion	47
	X6	Bonus for early Completion	48
	X7	Delay damages	48
	X12	Partnering	48
	X13	Performance bond	50
	X14	Advanced payment to the *Subcontractor*	50
	X15	Limitation of the *Subcontractor*'s liability for his design to reasonable skill and care	50
	X16	Retention	51
	X17	Low performance damages	51
	X18	Limitation of liability	51
	X20	Key Performance Indicators	52
	Y(UK)1	Project Bank Account	53
	Y(UK)2	The Housing Grants, Construction and Regeneration Act 1996	57
	Y(UK)3	The Contracts (Rights of Third Parties) Act 1999	57
	Z	*Additional conditions of subcontract*	57
Note		Options X8 to X11 and X19 are not used	
Schedule of Cost Components			58
Shorter Schedule of Cost Components			61
Subcontract Data			63
Index			76

FOREWORD

I was delighted to be asked to write the Foreword for the NEC3 Contracts.

I have followed the outstanding rise and success of NEC contracts for a number of years now, in particular during my tenure as the 146th President of the Institution of Civil Engineers, 2010/11.

In my position as UK Government's Chief Construction Adviser, I am working with Government and industry to ensure Britain's construction sector is equipped with the knowledge, skills and best practice it needs in its transition to a low carbon economy. I am promoting innovation in the sector, including in particular the use of Building Information Modelling (BIM) in public sector construction procurement; and the synergy and fit with the collaborative nature of NEC contracts is obvious. The Government's construction strategy is a very significant investment and NEC contracts will play an important role in setting high standards of contract preparation, management and the desirable behaviour of our industry.

In the UK, we are faced with having to deliver a 15–20 per cent reduction in the cost to the public sector of construction during the lifetime of this Parliament. Shifting mind-set, attitude and behaviour into best practice NEC processes will go a considerable way to achieving this.

Of course, NEC contracts are used successfully around the world in both public and private sector projects; this trend seems set to continue at an increasing pace. NEC contracts are, according to my good friend and NEC's creator Dr Martin Barnes CBE, about better management of projects. This is quite achievable and I encourage you to understand NEC contracts to the best you can and exploit the potential this offers us all.

Peter Hansford

UK Government's Chief Construction Adviser
Cabinet Office

PREFACE

The NEC contracts are the only suite of standard contracts designed to facilitate and encourage good management of the projects on which they are used. The experience of using NEC contracts around the world is that they really make a difference. Previously, standard contracts were written mainly as legal documents best left in the desk drawer until costly and delaying problems had occurred and there were lengthy arguments about who was to blame.

The language of NEC contracts is clear and simple, and the procedures set out are all designed to stimulate good management. Foresighted collaboration between all the contributors to the project is the aim. The contracts set out how the interfaces between all the organisations involved will be managed – from the client through the designers and main contractors to all the many subcontractors and suppliers.

Versions of the NEC contract are specific to the work of professional service providers such as project managers and designers, to main contractors, to subcontractors and to suppliers. The wide range of situations covered by the contracts means that they do not need to be altered to suit any particular situation.

The NEC contracts are the first to deal specifically and effectively with management of the inevitable risks and uncertainties which are encountered to some extent on all projects. Management of the expected is easy, effective management of the unexpected draws fully on the collaborative approach inherent in the NEC contracts.

Most people working on projects using the NEC contracts for the first time are hugely impressed by the difference between the confrontational characteristics of traditional contracts and the teamwork engendered by the NEC. The NEC does not include specific provisions for dispute avoidance. They are not necessary. Collaborative management itself is designed to avoid disputes and it really works.

It is common for the final account for the work on a project to be settled at the time when the work is finished. The traditional long period of expensive professional work after completion to settle final payments just is not needed.

The NEC contracts are truly a massive change for the better for the industries in which they are used.

Dr Martin Barnes CBE

Originator of the NEC contracts

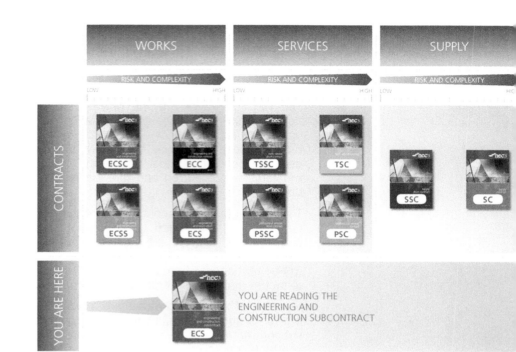

WORKS

SERVICES

SUPPLY

RISK AND COMPLEXITY

RISK AND COMPLEXITY

RISK AND COMPLEXITY

LOW   HIGH

LOW   HIGH

LOW   HIG

CONTRACTS

ECSC

ECC

TSSC

TSC

SSC

SC

ECSS

ECS

PSSC

PSC

YOU ARE HERE

ECS

YOU ARE READING THE
ENGINEERING AND
CONSTRUCTION SUBCONTRACT

ACKNOWLEDGEMENTS

The NEC first edition was produced by the Institution of Civil Engineers through its NEC Working Group.

The original NEC was designed and drafted by Dr Martin Barnes then of Coopers and Lybrand with the assistance of Professor J. G. Perry then of the University of Birmingham, T. W. Weddell then of Travers Morgan Management, T. H. Nicholson, Consultant to the Institution of Civil Engineers, A. Norman then of the University of Manchester Institute of Science and Technology and P. A. Baird, then Corporate Contracts Consultant, Eskom, South Africa.

The second edition of the NEC documents for engineering and construction contracts were produced by the Institution of Civil Engineers through its NEC Panel.

The third edition of the NEC Engineering and Construction Subcontract was mainly drafted by Drick Vernon with the assistance of members of the NEC Panel.

The members of the NEC Panel are:

P. Higgins, BSc, CEng, FICE, FCIArb (Chairman)
P. A. Baird, BSc, CEng, FICE, M(SA)ICE, MAPM
M. Barnes, BSc(Eng), PhD, FREng, FICE, FCIOB, CCMI, ACIArb, MBCS, FInstCES, FAPM
A. J. Bates, FRICS, MInstCES
A. J. M. Blackler, BA, LLB(Cantab), MCIArb
P. T. Cousins, BEng(Tech), DipArb, CEng, MICE, MCIArb, MCMI
L. T. Eames, BSc, FRICS, FCIOB
F. Forward, BA(Hons), DipArch, MSc(Const Law), RIBA, FCIArb
Professor J. G. Perry, MEng, PhD, CEng, FICE, MAPM
N. C. Shaw, FCIPS, CEng, MIMechE
T. W. Weddell, BSc, CEng, DIC, FICE, FIStructE, ACIArb

NEC Consultant:

R. A. Gerrard, BSc(Hons), MRICS, FCIArb, FCInstCES

Secretariat:

A. Cole, LLB, LLM, BL
J. M. Hawkins, BA(Hons), MSc
F. N. Vernon (Technical Adviser), BSc, CEng, MICE

AMENDMENTS JUNE 2006

The following amendments have been made to the June 2005 edition.

Page	Clause	Line	
10	32.1	4	deleted: 'and of notified early warning matters'
59	Contract Data Part one, 1.	3	added, '(with amendments June 2006)'
62	Contract Data Part one, 1.	23	deleted: 'If there are additional compensation events' and following 4 lines

AMENDMENTS JUNE 2013

The following amendments have been made to the June 2005 edition. Full details of all amendments are available on www.neccontract.com.

Page	Clause	Line	
11	40.1	1	replace: 'The subclauses in this clause only apply' with 'This clause only applies'
16	61.1		Text replaced
17	61.3 61.4		Text replaced Text replaced
18	62.6 63.1	2	'to this effect' replaced with 'of his failure' Text replaced delete final sentence: 'In all other . . . the event.' replace with 'In all other cases, the date is the date of the notification of the compensation event.'
19	64.4	2	'to this effect' replaced with 'of his failure'
25	91.4		Text replaced
28	63.14	2	deleted: 'instead of Defined Cost'
30	63.13	15	deleted: 'instead of Defined Cost'
33			New clause 63.14 added
37	63.13	15	deleted: 'instead of Defined Cost'
39			New clause 63.14 added

Page	Clause	Line	
44	W2.3 (7) W2.3 (8)		New sentence added at end New sentence added at end
45	W2.3 (12)		Text replaced
53	Y(UK)1	1	insert new clause: 'Project Bank Account'
55	Y(UK)1	1	insert new clause: 'Trust Deed'
56	Y(UK)1	1	insert new clause: 'Joining Deed'
57	Y2.1 (1) Y2.1 (2) Y2.3		Text replaced Text replaced Heading 'withhold payment' replaced with 'pay less', clause replaced
61		1	'only when Option A, B, C, D or E is used' replaced by 'in all Options'
62	41	9	Bullet point replaced
63	Subcontract Data Part one, 1.	3 6	'contract' replaced by 'subcontract' 'June 2006' date replaced with 'April 2013'
66	Optional statements	30	'21' replaced by '14'
71			New text added before 'If Option Z is used'
72	Contract Data Part two		New text added before 'If Option A or B is used'

SCHEDULE OF OPTIONS

The strategy for choosing the form of subcontract starts with a decision between five main Options, one of which must be chosen.

Option A	Priced subcontract with activity schedule
Option B	Priced subcontract with bill of quantities
Option C	Target subcontract with activity schedule
Option D	Target subcontract with bill of quantities
Option E	Cost reimbursable subcontract

One of the following dispute resolution Options must be selected to complete the chosen main Option.

Option W1	Dispute resolution procedure (used unless the United Kingdom Housing Grants, Construction and Regeneration Act 1996 applies).
Option W2	Dispute resolution procedure (used in the United Kingdom when the Housing Grants, Construction and Regeneration Act 1996 applies).

The following secondary Options should then be considered. It is not necessary to use any of them. Any combination other than those stated may be used.

Option X1	Price adjustment for inflation (used only with Options A, B, C and D)
Option X2	Changes in the law
Option X3	Multiple currencies (used only with Options A and B)
Option X4	Parent company guarantee
Option X5	Sectional Completion
Option X6	Bonus for early Completion
Option X7	Delay damages
Option X12	Partnering
Option X13	Performance bond
Option X14	Advanced payment to the *Subcontractor*
Option X15	Limitation of the *Subcontractor*'s liability for his design to reasonable skill and care
Option X16	Retention
Option X17	Low performance damages
Option X18	Limitation of liability
Option X20	Key Performance Indicators (not used with Option X12)

The following Options dealing with national legislation should be included if required.

Option Y(UK)1	Project Bank Account
Option Y(UK)2	The Housing Grants, Construction and Regeneration Act 1996
Option Y(UK)3	The Contracts (Rights of Third Parties) Act 1999
Option Z	*Additional conditions of subcontract*
Note	Options X8 to X11 and X19 are not used.

CORE CLAUSES

1 General

Actions   **10**

10.1   The *Contractor* and the *Subcontractor* shall act as stated in this subcontract and in a spirit of mutual trust and co-operation.

Identified and defined   **11**
terms   11.1   In these conditions of subcontract, terms identified in the Subcontract Data are in italics and defined terms have capital initials.

11.2   (1) The Accepted Programme is the programme identified in the Subcontract Data or is the latest programme accepted by the *Contractor*. The latest programme accepted by the *Contractor* supersedes previous Accepted Programmes.

(2) Completion is when the *Subcontractor* has

- done all the work which the Subcontract Works Information states he is to do by the Subcontract Completion Date and
- corrected notified Defects which would have prevented the *Employer* or the *Contractor* from using the *subcontract works* or Others from doing their work.

If the work which the *Subcontractor* is to do by the Subcontract Completion Date is not stated in the Subcontract Works Information, Completion is when the *Subcontractor* has done all the work necessary for the *Employer* or the *Contractor* to use the *subcontract works* or for Others to do their work.

(3) The Subcontract Completion Date is the *subcontract completion date* unless later changed in accordance with this subcontract.

(4) The Subcontract Date is the date when this subcontract came into existence.

(5) A Defect is

- a part of the *subcontract works* which is not in accordance with the Subcontract Works Information or
- a part of the *subcontract works* designed by the *Subcontractor* which is not in accordance with the applicable law or the *Subcontractor*'s design which the *Contractor* has accepted.

(6) The Defects Certificate is either a list of Defects that the *Contractor* has notified before the *defects date* which the *Subcontractor* has not corrected or, if there are no such Defects, a statement that there are none.

(7) Equipment is items provided by the *Subcontractor* and used by him to Provide the Subcontract Works and which the Subcontract Works Information does not require him to include in the *subcontract works*.

core clauses | main option clauses | secondary option clauses | cost components | subcontract data

core clauses

main option clauses

secondary option clauses

cost components

subcontract data

(8) The Fee is the sum of the amounts calculated by applying the *subsubcontracted fee percentage* to the Defined Cost of subsubcontracted work and the *direct fee percentage* to the Defined Cost of other work.

(9) A Key Date is the date by which work is to meet the Condition stated. The Key Date is the *key date* stated in the Subcontract Data and the Condition is the *condition* stated in the Subcontract Data unless later changed in accordance with this subcontract.

(10) Others are people or organisations who are not the *Employer*, the *Project Manager*, the *Supervisor*, the *Adjudicator*, the *Contractor, Subcontractor* or any employee, Subsubcontractor or supplier of the *Subcontractor*.

(11) The Parties are the *Contractor* and the *Subcontractor*.

(12) Plant and Materials are items intended to be included in the *subcontract works*.

(13) To Provide the Subcontract Works means to do the work necessary to complete the *subcontract works* in accordance with this subcontract and all incidental work, services and actions which this subcontract requires.

(14) The Risk Register is a register of the risks which are listed in the Subcontract Data and the risks which the *Contractor* or the *Subcontractor* has notified as an early warning matter. It includes a description of the risk and a description of the actions which are to be taken to avoid or reduce the risk.

(15) The Site is the area within the *boundaries of the site* and the volumes above and below it which are affected by work included in this subcontract.

(16) Site Information is information which

- describes the Site and its surroundings and
- is in the documents which the Subcontract Data states it is in.

(17) A Subsubcontractor is a person or organisation who has a contract with the *Subcontractor* to

- construct or install part of the *subcontract works,*
- provide a service necessary to Provide the Subcontract Works or
- supply Plant and Materials which the person or organisation has wholly or partly designed specifically for the *subcontract works.*

(18) The Working Areas are those parts of the *subcontract working areas* which are

- necessary for Providing the Subcontract Works and
- used only for work in this subcontract

unless later changed in accordance with this subcontract.

(19) Subcontract Works Information is information which either

- specifies and describes the *subcontract works* or
- states any constraints on how the *Subcontractor* Provides the Subcontract Works

and is either

- in the documents which the Subcontract Data states it is in or
- in an instruction given in accordance with this subcontract.

Interpretation and the law	**12**	
	12.1	In this subcontract, except where the context shows otherwise, words in the singular also mean in the plural and the other way round and words in the masculine also mean in the feminine and neuter.
	12.2	This subcontract is governed by the *law of the subcontract.*
	12.3	No change to this subcontract, unless provided by the *conditions of subcontract*, has effect unless it is has been agreed and confirmed in writing and signed by the Parties.
	12.4	This subcontract is the entire agreement between the Parties

Communications	**13**	
	13.1	Each instruction, certificate, submission, proposal, record, acceptance, notification, reply and other communication which this subcontract requires is communicated in a form which can be read, copied and recorded. Writing is in the *language of this subcontract.*
	13.2	A communication has effect when it is received at the last address notified by the recipient for receiving communications or, if none is notified, at the address of the recipient stated in the Subcontract Data.
	13.3	If this subcontract requires the *Contractor* or the *Subcontractor* to reply to a communication, unless otherwise stated in this subcontract, he replies within the *period for reply.*
	13.4	The *Contractor* replies to a communication submitted or resubmitted to him by the *Subcontractor* for acceptance. If his reply is not acceptance, the *Contractor* states his reasons and the *Subcontractor* resubmits the communication within the *period for reply* taking account of these reasons. A reason for withholding acceptance is that more information is needed in order to assess the *Subcontractor*'s submission fully.
	13.5	The *Contractor* may extend the *period for reply* to a communication if the *Contractor* and the *Subcontractor* agree to the extension before the reply is due. The *Contractor* notifies the *Subcontractor* of the extension which has been agreed.
	13.6	The *Contractor* issues his certificates to the *Subcontractor.*
	13.7	A notification which this subcontract requires is communicated separately from other communications.
	13.8	The *Contractor* may withhold acceptance of a submission by the *Subcontractor*. Withholding acceptance for a reason stated in this subcontract is not a compensation event.

The *Contractor*	**14**	
	14.1	The *Contractor*'s acceptance of a communication from the *Subcontractor* or of his work does not change the *Subcontractor*'s responsibility to Provide the Subcontract Works or his liability for his design.
	14.2	The *Contractor*, after notifying the *Subcontractor*, may delegate any of his actions and may cancel any delegation. A reference to an action of the *Contractor* in this subcontract includes an action by his delegate.
	14.3	The *Contractor* may give an instruction to the *Subcontractor* which changes the Subcontract Works Information or a Key Date.

Adding to the Working Areas	**15**	
	15.1	The *Subcontractor* may submit a proposal for adding an area to the Working Areas to the *Contractor* for acceptance. A reason for not accepting is that the proposed area is either not necessary for Providing the Subcontract Works or used for work not in this subcontract.

Sidebar: core clauses / main option clauses / secondary option clauses / cost components / subcontract data

core clauses

main option clauses

secondary option clauses

cost components

subcontract data

Early warning **16**

16.1 The *Subcontractor* and the *Contractor* give an early warning by notifying the other as soon as either becomes aware of any matter which could

- increase the total of the Prices,
- delay Completion,
- delay meeting a Key Date or
- impair the performance of the *subcontract works* in use.

The *Subcontractor* may give an early warning by notifying the *Contractor* of any other matter which could increase his total cost. The *Contractor* enters early warning matters in the Risk Register. Early warning of a matter for which a compensation event has previously been notified is not required.

16.2 Either the *Contractor* or the *Subcontractor* may instruct the other to attend a risk reduction meeting. Each may instruct other people to attend if the other agrees.

16.3 At a risk reduction meeting, those who attend co-operate in

- making and considering proposals for how the effect of the registered risks can be avoided or reduced,
- seeking solutions that will bring advantage to all those who will be affected,
- deciding on the actions which will be taken and who, in accordance with this subcontract, will take them and
- deciding which risks have now been avoided or have passed and can be removed from the Risk Register.

16.4 The *Contractor* revises the Risk Register to record the decisions made at each risk reduction meeting and issues the revised Risk Register to the *Subcontractor*. If a decision needs a change to the Subcontract Works Information, the *Contractor* instructs the change at the same time as he issues the revised Risk Register.

Ambiguities and **17**
inconsistencies 17.1 The *Contractor* or the *Subcontractor* notifies the other as soon as either becomes aware of an ambiguity or inconsistency in or between the documents which are part of this subcontract. The *Contractor* gives an instruction resolving the ambiguity or inconsistency.

Illegal and impossible **18**
requirements 18.1 The *Subcontractor* notifies the *Contractor* as soon as he considers that the Subcontract Works Information requires him to do anything which is illegal or impossible. If the *Contractor* agrees, he gives an instruction to change the Subcontract Works Information appropriately.

Prevention **19**

19.1 If an event occurs which

- stops the *Subcontractor* completing the *subcontract works* or
- stops the *Subcontractor* completing the *subcontract works* by the date shown on the Accepted Programme,

and which

- neither Party could prevent and
- an experienced subcontractor would have judged at the Subcontract Date to have such a small chance of occurring that it would have been unreasonable for him to have allowed for it,

the *Contractor* gives an instruction to the *Subcontractor* stating how he is to deal with the event.

2 The *Subcontractor*'s main responsibilities

Providing the Subcontract Works	**20**	
	20.1	The *Subcontractor* Provides the Subcontract Works in accordance with the Subcontract Works Information.

The *Subcontractor*'s design   **21**

21.1   The *Subcontractor* designs the parts of the *subcontract works* which the Subcontract Works Information states he is to design.

21.2   The *Subcontractor* submits the particulars of his design as the Subcontract Works Information requires to the *Contractor* for acceptance. A reason for not accepting the *Subcontractor*'s design is that it does not comply with either the Subcontract Works Information or the applicable law.

The *Subcontractor* does not proceed with the relevant work until the *Contractor* has accepted his design.

21.3   The *Subcontractor* may submit his design for acceptance in parts if the design of each part can be assessed fully.

Using the *Subcontractor*'s design   **22**

22.1   The *Employer* and the *Contractor* may use and copy the *Subcontractor*'s design for any purpose connected with construction, use, alteration or demolition of the *subcontract works* unless otherwise stated in the Subcontract Works Information and for other purposes as stated in the Subcontract Works Information.

Design of Equipment   **23**

23.1   The *Subcontractor* submits particulars of the design of an item of Equipment to the *Contractor* for acceptance if the *Contractor* instructs him to. A reason for not accepting is that the design of the item will not allow the *Subcontractor* to Provide the Subcontract Works in accordance with

- the Subcontract Works Information,
- the *Subcontractor*'s design which the *Contractor* has accepted or
- the applicable law.

People   **24**

24.1   The *Subcontractor* either employs each key person named to do the job stated in the Subcontract Data or employs a replacement person who has been accepted by the *Contractor*. The *Subcontractor* submits the name, relevant qualifications and experience of a proposed replacement person to the *Contractor* for acceptance. A reason for not accepting the person is that his relevant qualifications and experience are not as good as those of the person who is to be replaced.

24.2   The *Contractor* may, having stated his reasons, instruct the *Subcontractor* to remove an employee. The *Subcontractor* then arranges that, after one day, the employee has no further connection with the work included in this subcontract.

Working with the *Contractor* and Others   **25**

25.1   The *Subcontractor* co-operates with Others in obtaining and providing information which they need in connection with the *subcontract works*. He co-operates with Others and shares the Working Areas with them as stated in the Subcontract Works Information.

core clauses

main option clauses

secondary option clauses

cost components

subcontract data

25.2 The *Contractor* and the *Subcontractor* provide services and other things as stated in the Subcontract Works Information. Any cost incurred by the *Contractor* as a result of the *Subcontractor* not providing the services and other things he is to provide is assessed by the *Contractor* and paid by the *Subcontractor.*

25.3 If the *Contractor* decides that the work does not meet the Condition stated for a Key Date by the date stated and, as a result, the *Contractor* incurs additional cost either

- in carrying out work or
- by paying an additional amount to the *Employer* or Others in carrying out work

on the same project, the additional cost the which *Contractor* has paid or will incur is paid by the *Subcontractor*. The *Contractor* assesses the additional cost within four weeks of the date when the Condition for the Key Date is met. The *Contractor*'s right to recover the additional cost is his only right in these circumstances.

Subsubcontracting 26

26.1 If the *Subcontractor* subsubcontracts work, he is responsible for Providing the Subcontract Works as if he had not subsubcontracted. This subcontract applies as if a Subsubcontractor's employees and equipment were the *Subcontractor*'s.

26.2 The *Subcontractor* submits the name of each proposed Subsubcontractor to the *Contractor* for acceptance. A reason for not accepting the Subsubcontractor is that his appointment will not allow the *Subcontractor* to Provide the Subcontract Works. The *Subcontractor* does not appoint a proposed Subsubcontractor until the *Contractor* has accepted him.

26.3 The *Subcontractor* submits the proposed conditions of contract for each subsubcontract to the *Contractor* for acceptance unless

- an NEC contract is proposed or
- the *Contractor* has agreed that no submission is required.

The *Subcontractor* does not appoint a Subsubcontractor on the proposed subsubcontract conditions submitted until the *Contractor* has accepted them. A reason for not accepting them is that

- they will not allow the *Subcontractor* to Provide the Subcontract Works or
- they do not include a statement that the parties to the subsubcontract shall act in a spirit of mutual trust and co-operation.

Other responsibilities 27

27.1 The *Subcontractor* obtains approval of his design from Others where necessary.

27.2 The *Subcontractor* provides access to work being done and to Plant and Materials being stored for this subcontract for

- the *Contractor,*
- the *Project Manager,*
- the *Supervisor* and
- Others notified to him by the *Contractor* or the *Project Manager.*

27.3 The *Subcontractor* obeys an instruction which is in accordance with this subcontract and is given to him by the *Contractor.*

27.4 The *Subcontractor* acts in accordance with the health and safety requirements stated in the Subcontract Works Information.

3 Time

Starting, Completion and Key Dates	**30**	
	30.1	The *Subcontractor* does not start work on the Site until the first *subcontract access date* and does the work so that Completion is on or before the Subcontract Completion Date.
	30.2	The *Contractor* decides the date of Completion. The *Contractor* certifies Completion within one week of Completion.
	30.3	The *Subcontractor* does the work so that the Condition stated for each Key Date is met by the Key Date.

The programme **31**

31.1 If a programme is not identified in the Subcontract Data, the *Subcontractor* submits a first programme to the *Contractor* for acceptance within the period stated in the Subcontract Data.

31.2 The *Subcontractor* shows on each programme which he submits for acceptance

- the *subcontract starting date*, *subcontract access dates*, Key Dates and Subcontract Completion Date,
- planned Completion,
- the order and timing of the operations which the *Subcontractor* plans to do in order to Provide the Subcontract Works,
- the order and timing of the work of the *Employer,* the *Contractor* and Others as last agreed with them by the *Subcontractor* or, if not so agreed, as stated in the Subcontract Works Information,
- the dates when the *Subcontractor* plans to meet each Condition stated for the Key Dates and to complete other work needed to allow the *Employer,* the *Contractor* and Others to do their work,
- provisions for

  - float,
  - time risk allowances,
  - health and safety requirements and
  - the procedures set out in this subcontract,

- the dates when, in order to Provide the Subcontract Works in accordance with his programme, the *Subcontractor* will need

  - access to a part of the Site if later than its *subcontract access date*,
  - acceptances,
  - Plant and Materials and other things to be provided by the *Employer* and the *Contractor* and
  - information from Others,

- for each operation, a statement of how the *Subcontractor* plans to do the work identifying the principal Equipment and other resources which he plans to use and
- other information which the Subcontract Works Information requires the *Subcontractor* to show on a programme submitted for acceptance.

31.3 Within two weeks of the *Subcontractor* submitting a programme to him for acceptance, the *Contractor* either accepts the programme or notifies the *Subcontractor* of his reasons for not accepting it. A reason for not accepting a programme is that

- the *Subcontractor*'s plans which it shows are not practicable,
- it does not show the information which this subcontract requires,
- it does not represent the *Subcontractor*'s plans realistically or
- it does not comply with the Subcontract Works Information.

core clauses

main option clauses

secondary option clauses

cost components

subcontract data

Revising the programme **32**

32.1   The *Subcontractor* shows on each revised programme

- the actual progress achieved on each operation and its effect upon the timing of the remaining work,
- the effects of implemented compensation events,
- how the *Subcontractor* plans to deal with any delays and to correct notified Defects and
- any other changes which the *Subcontractor* proposes to make to the Accepted Programme.

32.2   The *Subcontractor* submits a revised programme to the *Contractor* for acceptance

- within the *period for reply* after the *Contractor* has instructed him to,
- when the *Subcontractor* chooses to and, in any case,
- at no longer interval than the interval stated in the Subcontract Data from the *subcontract starting date* until Completion of the whole of the *subcontract works*.

Access to and use of the Site **33**

33.1   The *Contractor* allows access to and use of each part of the Site to the *Subcontractor* which is necessary for the work included in this subcontract. Access and use is allowed on or before the later of its *subcontract access date* and the date for access shown on the Accepted Programme.

Instructions to stop or not to start work **34**

34.1   The *Contractor* may instruct the *Subcontractor* to stop or not to start any work and may later instruct him that he may re-start or start it.

Take over **35**

35.1   The *Contractor* need not take over the *subcontract works* before the Sub-contract Completion Date if it is stated in the Subcontract Data that he is not willing to do so. Otherwise the *Contractor* takes over the *subcontract works* not later than two weeks after Completion.

35.2   The *Employer* or the *Contractor* may use any part of the *subcontract works* before Completion has been certified. If he does so, the *Contractor* takes over the part of the *subcontract works* when the *Employer* or the *Contractor* begins to use it except if the use is

- for a reason stated in the Subcontract Works Information or
- to suit the *Subcontractor*'s method of working.

35.3   The *Contractor* certifies the date upon which he takes over any part of the *subcontract works* and its extent within two weeks of the date.

Acceleration **36**

36.1   The *Contractor* may instruct the *Subcontractor* to submit a quotation for an acceleration to achieve Completion before the Subcontract Completion Date. The *Contractor* states changes to the Key Dates to be included in the quotation. A quotation for an acceleration comprises proposed changes to the Prices and a revised programme showing the earlier Subcontract Completion Date and the changed Key Dates. The *Subcontractor* submits details of his assessment with each quotation.

36.2   The *Subcontractor* submits a quotation or gives his reasons for not doing so within the *period for reply*.

4 Testing and Defects

Tests and inspections 40

40.1 This clause only applies to tests and inspections required by the Subcontract Works Information or the applicable law.

40.2 The *Subcontractor,* the *Contractor* and the *Employer* provide materials, facilities and samples for tests and inspections as stated in the Subcontract Works Information.

40.3 The *Subcontractor* and the *Contractor* each notifies the other of each of his tests and inspections before it starts and afterwards notifies the other of its results. The *Subcontractor* notifies the *Contractor* in time for a test or inspection to be arranged and done before doing work which would obstruct the test or inspection. The *Contractor* and the *Supervisor* may watch any test done by the *Subcontractor.*

40.4 If a test or inspection shows that any work has a Defect, the *Subcontractor* corrects the Defect and the test or inspection is repeated.

40.5 The *Contractor* does his tests and inspections without causing unnecessary delay to the work or to a payment which is conditional upon a test or inspection being successful. A payment which is conditional upon a *Contractor*'s or *Supervisor*'s test or inspection being successful becomes due at the later of the *defects date* and the end of the last *defect correction period* if

- the *Contractor* or the *Supervisor* has not done the test or inspection and
- the delay to the test or inspection is not the *Subcontractor*'s fault.

40.6 The *Contractor* assesses the cost incurred by him in repeating a test or inspection after a Defect is found. The *Subcontractor* pays the amount assessed.

Testing and inspection 41
before delivery 41.1 The *Subcontractor* does not bring to the Working Areas those Plant and Materials which the Subcontract Works Information states are to be tested or inspected before delivery until the *Contractor* has notified the *Subcontractor* that they have passed the test or inspection.

Searching for and notifying 42
Defects 42.1 Until the *defects date*, the *Contractor* may instruct the *Subcontractor* to search for a Defect. He gives his reason for the search with his instruction. Searching may include

- uncovering, dismantling, re-covering and re-erecting work,
- providing facilities, materials and samples for tests and inspections done by the *Contractor* or the *Supervisor* and
- doing tests and inspections which the Subcontract Works Information does not require.

42.2 Until the *defects date*, the *Contractor* promptly notifies the *Subcontractor* of each Defect as soon as he finds it and the *Subcontractor* promptly notifies the *Contractor* of each Defect as soon as he finds it.

Correcting Defects 43

43.1 The *Subcontractor* corrects a Defect whether or not the *Contractor* notifies him of it.

43.2 The *Subcontractor* corrects a notified Defect before the end of the *defect correction period*. The *defect correction period* begins at Completion for Defects notified before Completion and when the Defect is notified for other Defects.

(side tab) core clauses | main option clauses | secondary option clauses | cost components | subcontract data

43.3 The *Contractor* issues the Defects Certificate at the later of the *defects date* and the end of the last *defect correction period*. The *Employer*'s or the *Contractor*'s rights in respect of a Defect which the *Contractor* has not found or notified are not affected by the issue of the Defects Certificate.

43.4 The *Contractor* arranges for the *Employer* and the *Contractor* to allow the *Subcontractor* access to and use of a part of the *subcontract works* which the *Contractor* has taken over if they are needed for correcting a Defect. In this case the *defect correction period* begins when the necessary access and use have been provided.

Accepting Defects 44

44.1 The *Subcontractor* and the *Contractor* may each propose to the other that the Subcontract Works Information should be changed so that a Defect does not have to be corrected.

44.2 If the *Subcontractor* and the *Contractor* are prepared to consider the change, the *Subcontractor* submits a quotation for reduced Prices or an earlier Subcontract Completion Date or both to the *Contractor* for acceptance. If the *Contractor* accepts the quotation, he gives an instruction to change the Subcontract Works Information, the Prices and the Subcontract Completion Date accordingly.

Uncorrected Defects 45

45.1 If the *Subcontractor* is given access in order to correct a notified Defect but he has not corrected it within its *defect correction period*, the *Contractor* assesses the cost to him of having the Defect corrected by other people and the *Subcontractor* pays this amount. The Subcontract Works Information is treated as having been changed to accept the Defect.

45.2 If the *Subcontractor* is not given access in order to correct a notified Defect before the *defects date*, the *Contractor* assesses the cost to the *Subcontractor* of correcting the Defect and the *Subcontractor* pays this amount. The Subcontract Works Information is treated as having been changed to accept the Defect.

5 Payment

Assessing the amount due **50**

50.1 The *Contractor* assesses the amount due at each assessment date. The first assessment date is decided by the *Contractor* to suit the procedures of the Parties and is not later than the *assessment interval* after the *subcontract starting date*. Later assessment dates occur

- at the end of each *assessment interval* until four weeks after the *Contractor* issues the Defects Certificate and
- at Completion of the whole of the *subcontract works*.

50.2 The amount due is

- the Price for Work Done to Date,
- plus other amounts to be paid to the *Subcontractor*,
- less amounts to be paid by or retained from the *Subcontractor*.

Any tax which the law requires the *Contractor* to pay to the *Subcontractor* is included in the amount due.

50.3 If no programme is identified in the Subcontract Data, one quarter of the Price for Work Done to Date is retained in assessments of the amount due until the *Subcontractor* has submitted a first programme to the *Contractor* for acceptance showing the information which this subcontract requires.

50.4 In assessing the amount due, the *Contractor* considers any application for payment the *Subcontractor* has submitted on or before the assessment date. The *Contractor* gives the *Subcontractor* details of how the amount due has been assessed.

50.5 The *Contractor* corrects any wrongly assessed amount due in a later payment certificate.

Payment **51**

51.1 The *Contractor* certifies a payment within two weeks of each assessment date. The first payment is the amount due. Other payments are the change in the amount due since the last payment certificate. A payment is made by the *Subcontractor* to the *Contractor* if the change reduces the amount due. Other payments are made by the *Contractor* to the *Subcontractor*. Payments are in the *currency of this subcontract* unless otherwise stated in this subcontract.

51.2 Each certified payment is made within four weeks of the assessment date or, if a different period is stated in the Subcontract Data, within the period stated. If a certified payment is late, or if a payment is late because the *Contractor* does not issue a certificate which he should issue, interest is paid on the late payment. Interest is assessed from the date by which the late payment should have been made until the date when the late payment is made, and is included in the first assessment after the late payment is made.

51.3 If an amount due is corrected in a later certificate either

- by the *Contractor* in relation to a mistake or a compensation event or
- following a decision of the *Adjudicator* or the *tribunal*,

interest on the correcting amount is paid. Interest is assessed from the date when the incorrect amount was certified until the date when the correcting amount is certified and is included in the assessment which includes the correcting amount.

51.4 Interest is calculated on a daily basis at the *interest rate* and is compounded annually.

core clauses

main option clauses

secondary option clauses

cost components

subcontract data

Defined Cost **52**

52.1 All the *Subcontractor*'s costs which are not included in the Defined Cost are treated as included in the Fee. Defined Cost includes only amounts calculated using rates and percentages stated in the Subcontract Data and other amounts at open market or competitively tendered prices with deductions for all discounts, rebates and taxes which can be recovered.

6 Compensation events

Compensation events **60**

60.1 The following are compensation events.

(1) The *Contractor* gives an instruction changing the Subcontract Works Information except

- a change made in order to accept a Defect or
- a change to the Subcontract Works Information provided by the *Subcontractor* for his design which is made either at his request or to comply with other Subcontract Works Information provided by the *Contractor*.

(2) The *Contractor* does not allow access to and use of a part of the Site by the later of its *subcontract access date* and the date shown on the Accepted Programme.

(3) The *Contractor* does not provide something which he is to provide by the date for providing it shown on the Accepted Programme.

(4) The *Contractor* gives an instruction to stop or not to start any work or to change a Key Date.

(5) The *Employer,* the *Contractor* or Others

- do not work within the times shown on the Accepted Programme,
- do not work within the conditions stated in the Subcontract Works Information or
- carry out work on the Site that is not stated in the Subcontract Works Information.

(6) The *Contractor* does not reply to a communication from the *Subcontractor* within the period required by this subcontract.

(7) The *Contractor* gives an instruction for dealing with an object of value or of historical or other interest found within the Site.

(8) The *Contractor* changes a decision which he has previously communicated to the *Subcontractor*.

(9) The *Contractor* withholds an acceptance (other than acceptance of a quotation for acceleration or for not correcting a Defect) for a reason not stated in this subcontract.

(10) The *Contractor* instructs the *Subcontractor* to search for a Defect and no Defect is found unless the search is needed only because the *Subcontractor* gave insufficient notice of doing work obstructing a required test or inspection.

(11) A test or inspection done by the *Contractor* or the *Supervisor* causes unnecessary delay.

(12) The *Subcontractor* encounters physical conditions which

- are within the Site,
- are not weather conditions and
- an experienced subcontractor would have judged at the Subcontract Date to have such a small chance of occurring that it would have been unreasonable for him to have allowed for them.

Only the difference between the physical conditions encountered and those for which it would have been reasonable to have allowed is taken into account in assessing a compensation event.

(13) A *weather measurement* is recorded

- within a calendar month,
- before the Subcontract Completion Date for the whole of the *subcontract works* and
- at the place stated in the Subcontract Data

the value of which, by comparison with the *weather data*, is shown to occur on average less frequently than once in ten years.

Only the difference between the *weather measurement* and the weather which the *weather data* show to occur on average less frequently than once in ten years is taken into account in assessing a compensation event.

(14) An event which is an *Employer*'s or a *Contractor*'s risk stated in this subcontract.

(15) The *Contractor* certifies take over of a part of the *subcontract works* before both Completion and the Subcontract Completion Date.

(16) The *Contractor* or the *Employer* does not provide materials, facilities and samples for tests and inspections as stated in the Subcontract Works Information.

(17) The *Contractor* notifies a correction to an assumption which he has stated about a compensation event.

(18) A breach of subcontract by the *Contractor* which is not one of the other compensation events in this subcontract.

(19) An event which

- stops the *Subcontractor* completing the *subcontract works* or
- stops the *Subcontractor* completing the *subcontract works* by the date shown on the Accepted Programme,

and which

- neither Party could prevent,
- an experienced subcontractor would have judged at the Subcontract Date to have such a small chance of occurring that it would have been unreasonable for him to have allowed for it and
- is not one of the other compensation events stated in this subcontract.

60.2 In judging the physical conditions for the purpose of assessing a compensation event, the *Subcontractor* is assumed to have taken into account

- the Site Information,
- publicly available information referred to in the Site Information,
- information obtainable from a visual inspection of the Site and
- other information which an experienced subcontractor could reasonably be expected to have or to obtain.

60.3 If there is an ambiguity or inconsistency within the Site Information (including the information referred to in it), the *Subcontractor* is assumed to have taken into account the physical conditions more favourable to doing the work.

Notifying compensation events **61**

61.1 For compensation events which arise from the *Contractor* giving an instruction, issuing a certificate, changing an earlier decision or correcting an assumption, the *Contractor* notifies the *Subcontractor* of the compensation event at the time of that communication. He also instructs the *Subcontractor* to submit quotations, unless the event arises from a fault of the *Subcontractor* or quotations have already been submitted. The *Subcontractor* puts the instruction or changed decision into effect.

61.2 The *Contractor* may instruct the *Subcontractor* to submit quotations for a proposed instruction or a proposed changed decision. The *Subcontractor* does not put a proposed instruction or a proposed changed decision into effect.

61.3 The *Subcontractor* notifies the *Contractor* of an event which has happened or which he expects to happen as a compensation event if

- the *Subcontractor* believes that the event is a compensation event and
- the *Contractor* has not notified the event to the *Subcontractor*.

If the *Subcontractor* does not notify a compensation event within seven weeks of becoming aware of the event, he is not entitled to a change in the Prices, the Subcontract Completion Date or a Key Date unless the event arises from the *Contractor* giving an instruction, issuing a certificate, changing an earlier decision or correcting an assumption.

61.4 If the *Contractor* decides that an event notified by the *Subcontractor*

- arises from a fault of the *Subcontractor*,
- has not happened and is not expected to happen,
- has no effect upon Defined Cost, Completion or meeting a Key Date or
- is not one of the compensation events stated in this subcontract

he notifies the *Subcontractor* of his decision that the Prices, the Subcontract Completion Date and the Key Dates are not to be changed. If the *Contractor* decides otherwise, he notifies the *Subcontractor* accordingly and instructs him to submit quotations.

The *Contractor* notifies his decision to the *Subcontractor* and, if his decision is that the Prices, the Subcontract Completion Date or the Key Dates are to be changed, instructs him to submit quotations before the end of either

- two weeks after the *Subcontractor*'s notification or
- a longer period to which the *Subcontractor* has agreed.

If the *Contractor* does not notify his decision, the *Subcontractor* may notify the *Contractor* of his failure. A failure by the *Contractor* to reply within three weeks of this notification is treated as acceptance by the *Contractor* that the event is a compensation event and an instruction to submit quotations.

61.5 If the *Contractor* decides that the *Subcontractor* did not give an early warning of the event which an experienced subcontractor could have given, he notifies this decision to the *Subcontractor* when he instructs him to submit quotations.

61.6 If the *Contractor* decides that the effects of a compensation event are too uncertain to be forecast reasonably, he states assumptions about the nature of the event in his instruction to the *Subcontractor* to submit quotations. Assessment of the event is based on these assumptions. If any of them is later found to have been wrong, the *Contractor* notifies a correction.

61.7 A compensation event is not notified after the *defects date*.

Quotations for **62**
compensation events **62.1** After discussing with the *Subcontractor* different ways of dealing with the compensation event which are practicable, the *Contractor* may instruct the *Subcontractor* to submit alternative quotations. The *Subcontractor* submits the required quotations to the *Contractor* and may submit quotations for other methods of dealing with the compensation event which he considers practicable.

62.2 Quotations for compensation events comprise proposed changes to the Prices and any delay to the Subcontract Completion Date and Key Dates assessed by the *Subcontractor*. The *Subcontractor* submits details of his assessment with each quotation. If the programme for remaining work is altered by the compensation event, the *Subcontractor* includes the alterations to the Accepted Programme in his quotation.

core clauses

main option clauses

secondary option clauses

cost components

subcontract data

62.3 The *Subcontractor* submits quotations within one week of being instructed to do so by the *Contractor*. The *Contractor* replies within four weeks of the submission. His reply is

- an instruction to submit a revised quotation,
- an acceptance of a quotation,
- a notification that a proposed instruction will not be given or a proposed changed decision will not be made or
- a notification that he will be making his own assessment.

62.4 The *Contractor* instructs the *Subcontractor* to submit a revised quotation only after explaining his reasons for doing so to the *Subcontractor*. The *Subcontractor* submits the revised quotation within one week of being instructed to do so.

62.5 The *Contractor* extends the time allowed for

- the *Subcontractor* to submit quotations for a compensation event and
- the *Contractor* to reply to a quotation

if the *Contractor* and the *Subcontractor* agree to the extension before the submission or reply is due. The *Contractor* notifies the extension that has been agreed to the *Subcontractor*.

62.6 If the *Contractor* does not reply to a quotation within the time allowed, the *Subcontractor* may notify the *Contractor* of his failure. If the *Subcontractor* submitted more than one quotation for the compensation event, he states in his notification which quotation he proposes is to be accepted. If the *Contractor* does not reply to the notification within three weeks, and unless the quotation is for a proposed instruction or a proposed changed decision, the *Subcontractor*'s notification is treated as acceptance of the quotation by the *Contractor*.

Assessing compensation events 63

63.1 The changes to the Prices are assessed as the effect of the compensation event upon

- the actual Defined Cost of the work already done,
- the forecast Defined Cost of the work not yet done and
- the resulting Fee.

If the compensation event arose from the *Contractor* giving an instruction, issuing a certificate, changing an earlier decision or correcting an assumption, the date which divides the work already done from the work not yet done is the date of that communication. In all other cases, the date is the date of the notification of the compensation event.

63.2 If the effect of a compensation event is to reduce the total Defined Cost, the Prices are not reduced except as stated in this subcontract.

63.3 A delay to the Subcontract Completion Date is assessed as the length of time that, due to the compensation event, planned Completion is later than planned Completion as shown on the Accepted Programme. A delay to a Key Date is assessed as the length of time that, due to the compensation event, the planned date when the Condition stated for a Key Date will be met is later than the date shown on the Accepted Programme.

63.4 The rights of the *Contractor* and the *Subcontractor* to changes to the Prices, the Subcontract Completion Date and the Key Dates are their only rights in respect of a compensation event.

63.5 If the *Contractor* has notified the *Subcontractor* of his decision that the *Subcontractor* did not give an early warning of a compensation event which an experienced subcontractor could have given, the event is assessed as if the *Subcontractor* had given early warning.

63.6 Assessment of the effect of a compensation event includes risk allowances for cost and time for matters which have a significant chance of occurring and are at the *Subcontractor*'s risk under this subcontract.

63.7 Assessments are based upon the assumptions that the *Subcontractor* reacts competently and promptly to the compensation event, that any Defined Cost and time due to the event are reasonably incurred and that the Accepted Programme can be changed.

63.8 A compensation event which is an instruction to change the Subcontract Works Information in order to resolve an ambiguity or inconsistency is assessed as if the Prices, the Subcontract Completion Date and the Key Dates were for the interpretation most favourable to the Party which did not provide the Subcontract Works Information.

63.9 If a change to the Subcontract Works Information makes the description of the Condition for a Key Date incorrect, the *Contractor* corrects the description. This correction is taken into account in assessing the compensation event for the change to the Subcontract Works Information.

The *Contractor*'s **64**
assessments **64.1** The *Contractor* assesses a compensation event

- if the *Subcontractor* has not submitted a quotation and details of his assessment within the time allowed,
- if the *Contractor* decides that the *Subcontractor* has not assessed the compensation event correctly in a quotation and he does not instruct the *Subcontractor* to submit a revised quotation,
- if, when the *Subcontractor* submits quotations for a compensation event, he has not submitted a programme or alterations to a programme which this subcontract requires him to submit or
- if, when the *Subcontractor* submits quotations for a compensation event, the *Contractor* has not accepted the *Subcontractor*'s latest programme for one of the reasons stated in this subcontract.

64.2 The *Contractor* assesses a compensation event using his own assessment of the programme for the remaining work if

- there is no Accepted Programme or
- the *Subcontractor* has not submitted a programme or alterations to a programme for acceptance as required by this subcontract.

64.3 The *Contractor* notifies the *Subcontractor* of his assessment of a compensation event and gives him details of it within the period allowed for the *Subcontractor*'s submission of his quotation for the same event. This period starts when the need for the *Contractor*'s assessment becomes apparent.

64.4 If the *Contractor* does not assess a compensation event within the time allowed, the *Subcontractor* may notify the *Contractor* of his failure. If the *Subcontractor* submitted more than one quotation for the compensation event, he states in his notification which quotation he proposes is to be accepted. If the *Contractor* does not reply within three weeks of this notification the notification is treated as acceptance of the *Subcontractor*'s quotation by the *Contractor*.

Implementing **65**
compensation events **65.1** A compensation event is implemented when

- the *Contractor* notifies his acceptance of the *Subcontractor*'s quotation,
- the *Contractor* notifies the *Subcontractor* of his own assessment or
- a *Subcontractor*'s quotation is treated as having been accepted by the *Contractor*.

65.2 The assessment of a compensation event is not revised if a forecast upon which it is based is shown by later recorded information to have been wrong.

7 Title

core clauses
main option clauses
secondary option clauses
cost components
subcontract data

The *Contractor*'s title to Plant and Materials	**70**	
	70.1	Whatever title the *Subcontractor* has to Plant and Materials which is outside the Working Areas passes to the *Contractor* if the *Contractor* has marked it as for this subcontract.
	70.2	Whatever title the *Subcontractor* has to Plant and Materials passes to the *Contractor* if it has been brought within the Working Areas. The title to Plant and Materials passes back to the *Subcontractor* if it is removed from the Working Areas with the *Contractor*'s permission.
Marking Equipment, Plant and Materials outside the Working Areas	**71**	
	71.1	The *Contractor* marks Equipment, Plant and Materials which are outside the Working Areas if

- this subcontract identifies them for payment and
- the *Subcontractor* has prepared them for marking as the Subcontract Works Information requires.

Removing Equipment	**72**	
	72.1	The *Subcontractor* removes Equipment from the Site when it is no longer needed unless the *Contractor* allows it to be left in the *subcontract works*.
Objects and materials within the Site	**73**	
	73.1	The *Subcontractor* has no title to an object of value or of historical or other interest within the Site. The *Subcontractor* notifies the *Contractor* when such an object is found and the *Contractor* instructs the *Subcontractor* how to deal with it. The *Subcontractor* does not move the object without instructions.
	73.2	The *Subcontractor* has title to materials from excavation and demolition only as stated in the Subcontract Works Information.

8 Risks and insurance

Employer's and
Contractor's risks

80

80.1   The following are _Employer_'s and _Contractor_'s risks.

- Claims, proceedings, compensation and costs payable which are due to

  - use or occupation of the Site by the _works_ or for the purpose of the _works_ which is the unavoidable result of the _works_,
  - negligence, breach of statutory duty or interference with any legal right by the _Employer_ or the _Contractor_ or by any person employed by or contracted to them except the _Subcontractor_ or
  - a fault of the _Employer_ or the _Contractor_ or a fault in their designs.

- Loss of or damage to Plant and Materials supplied to the _Subcontractor_ by the _Employer_ or _Contractor_, or by Others on the _Employer_'s or _Contractor_'s behalf, until the _Subcontractor_ has received and accepted them.

- Loss of or damage to the _works_, Plant and Materials due to

  - war, civil war, rebellion, revolution, insurrection, military or usurped power,
  - strikes, riots and civil commotion not confined to the _Subcontractor_'s employees or
  - radioactive contamination.

- Loss of or wear or damage to the parts of the _subcontract works_ taken over by the _Contractor_, except loss, wear or damage occurring before the issue of the Defects Certificate which is due to

  - a Defect which existed at take over,
  - an event occurring before take over which was not itself an _Employer_'s or _Contractor_'s risk or
  - the activities of the _Subcontractor_ on the Site after take over.

- Loss of or wear or damage to the _subcontract works_ and any Equipment, Plant and Materials retained on the Site by the _Employer_ or _Contractor_ after a termination, except loss, wear or damage due to the activities of the _Subcontractor_ on the Site after the termination.

- Additional _Employer_'s or _Contractor_'s risks stated in the Subcontract Data.

The _Subcontractor_'s risks

81

81.1   From the _subcontract starting date_ until the Defects Certificate has been issued, the risks which are not carried by the _Employer_ or the _Contractor_ are carried by the _Subcontractor_.

Repairs

82

82.1   Until the Defects Certificate has been issued and unless otherwise instructed by the _Contractor,_ the _Subcontractor_ promptly replaces loss of and repairs damage to the _subcontract works_, Plant and Materials.

Indemnity

83

83.1   Each Party indemnifies the other against claims, proceedings, compensation and costs due to an event which is at his risk. The _Contractor_ indemnifies the _Subcontractor_ against all claims and liabilities against which the _Employer_ indemnifies the _Contractor_ under the main contract.

83.2   The liability of the _Subcontractor_ to indemnify the _Contractor_ is reduced if events at the _Employer_'s or _Contractor_'s risk contributed to the claims, proceedings, compensation and costs. The reduction is in proportion to the extent that events which were at the _Employer_'s or _Contractor_'s risk contributed, taking into account each Party's responsibilities under this subcontract.

core clauses

main option clauses

secondary option clauses

cost components

subcontract data

83.3 The liability of the *Contractor* to indemnify the *Subcontractor* is reduced if events at the *Subcontractor*'s risk contributed to the claims, proceedings, compensation and costs. The reduction is in proportion to the extent that events which were at the *Subcontractor*'s risk contributed, taking into account each Party's responsibilities under this subcontract.

Insurance cover 84

84.1 The *Subcontractor* provides the insurances stated in the Insurance Table except any insurance which the *Employer* or the *Contractor* is to provide as stated in the Subcontract Data. The *Subcontractor* provides additional insurances as stated in the Subcontract Data.

84.2 The insurances are in the joint names of the Parties and provide cover for events which are at the *Subcontractor*'s risk from the *subcontract starting date* until the Defects Certificate or a termination certificate has been issued.

INSURANCE TABLE

Insurance against	Minimum amount of cover or minimum limit of indemnity
Loss of or damage to the *subcontract works*, Plant and Materials	The replacement cost, including the amount stated in the Subcontract Data for the replacement of any Plant and Materials provided by the *Employer* or the *Contractor*
Loss of or damage to Equipment	The replacement cost
Liability for loss of or damage to property (except the *subcontract works*, Plant and Materials and Equipment) and liability for bodily injury to or death of a person (not an employee of the *Subcontractor*) caused by activity in connection with this subcontract	The amount stated in the Subcontract Data for any one event with cross liability so that the insurance applies to the Parties separately
Liability for death of or bodily injury to employees of the *Subcontractor* arising out of and in the course of their employment in connection with this subcontract	The greater of the amount required by the applicable law and the amount stated in the Subcontract Data for any one event

Insurance policies 85

85.1 Before the *subcontract starting date* and on each renewal of the insurance policy until the *defects date*, the *Subcontractor* submits to the *Contractor* for acceptance certificates which state that the insurance required by this subcontract is in force. The certificates are signed by the *Subcontractor*'s insurer or insurance broker. A reason for not accepting the certificates is that they do not comply with this subcontract.

85.2 Insurance policies include a waiver by the insurers of their subrogation rights against directors and other employees of every insured except where there is fraud.

85.3 The Parties comply with the terms and conditions of the insurance policies.

85.4 Any amount not recovered from an insurer is borne by the *Employer* or *Contractor* for events which are at their risk and by the *Subcontractor* for events which are at his risk.

If the *Subcontractor* does not insure	**86**	
	86.1	The *Contractor* may insure a risk which this subcontract requires the *Subcontractor* to insure if the *Subcontractor* does not submit a required certificate. The cost of this insurance to the *Contractor* is paid by the *Subcontractor*.
Insurance by the *Employer* or the *Contractor*	**87**	
	87.1	The *Contractor* submits policies and certificates for insurances provided by the *Employer* or the *Contractor* to the *Subcontractor* for acceptance before the *subcontract starting date* and afterwards as the *Subcontractor* instructs. The *Subcontractor* accepts the policies and certificates if they comply with this subcontract.
	87.2	The *Subcontractor*'s acceptance of an insurance policy or certificate provided by the *Employer* or *Contractor* does not change the responsibility of the *Employer* or *Contractor* to provide the insurances stated in the Subcontract Data.
	87.3	The *Subcontractor* may insure a risk which this subcontract requires the *Employer* or *Contractor* to insure if the *Contractor* does not submit a required policy or certificate. The cost of this insurance to the *Subcontractor* is paid by the *Contractor*.

core clauses

main option clauses

secondary option clauses

cost components

subcontract data

9 Termination

core
clauses

main
option clauses

secondary
option clauses

cost
components

subcontract
data

Termination 90

90.1 If either Party wishes to terminate the *Subcontractor*'s obligation to Provide the Subcontract Works he notifies the other Party giving details of his reason for terminating. The *Contractor* issues a termination certificate promptly if the reason complies with this subcontract.

90.2 The *Subcontractor* may terminate only for a reason identified in the Termination Table. The *Contractor* may terminate for any reason. The procedures followed and the amounts due on termination are in accordance with the Termination Table.

TERMINATION TABLE

Terminating Party	Reason	Procedure	Amount due
The *Contractor*	A reason other than R1–R21	P1 and P2	A1, A2 and A4
	R1–R15 or R18	P1, P2 and P3	A1 and A3
	R17 or R20	P1 and P3	A1 and A2
	R21	P1 and P4	A1 and A2
The *Subcontractor*	R1–R10, R16 or R19	P1 and P4	A1, A2 and A4
	R17 or R20	P1 and P4	A1 and A2

90.3 The procedures for termination are implemented immediately after the *Contractor* has issued a termination certificate.

90.4 Within fourteen weeks of termination, the *Contractor* certifies a final payment to or from the *Subcontractor* which is the *Contractor*'s assessment of the amount due on termination less the total of previous payments. Payment is made within four weeks of the *Contractor*'s certificate.

90.5 After a termination certificate has been issued, the *Subcontractor* does no further work necessary to Provide the Subcontract Works.

Reasons for termination 91

91.1 Either Party may terminate if the other Party has done one of the following or its equivalent.

- If the other Party is an individual and has
  - presented his petition for bankruptcy (R1),
  - had a bankruptcy order made against him (R2),
  - had a receiver appointed over his assets (R3) or
  - made an arrangement with his creditors (R4).
- If the other Party is a company or partnership and has
  - had a winding-up order made against it (R5),
  - had a provisional liquidator appointed to it (R6),
  - passed a resolution for winding-up (other than in order to amalgamate or reconstruct) (R7),
  - had an administration order made against it (R8),
  - had a receiver, receiver and manager, or administrative receiver appointed over the whole or a substantial part of its undertaking or assets (R9) or
  - made an arrangement with its creditors (R10).

91.2 The *Contractor* may terminate if he has notified that the *Subcontractor* has defaulted in one of the following ways and not put the default right within three weeks of the notification.

- Substantially failed to comply with his obligations (R11).
- Not provided a bond or guarantee which this subcontract requires (R12).
- Appointed a Subsubcontractor for substantial work before the *Contractor* has accepted the Subsubcontractor (R13).

91.3 The *Contractor* may terminate if he has notified that the *Subcontractor* has defaulted in one of the following ways and not stopped defaulting within three weeks of the notification.

- Substantially hindered the *Employer,* the *Contractor* or Others (R14).
- Substantially broken a health or safety regulation (R15).

91.4 The *Subcontractor* may terminate if the *Contractor* has not paid an amount due under the contract within eleven weeks of the date that it should have been paid (R16).

91.5 Either Party may terminate if the Parties have been released under the law from further performance of the whole of this subcontract (R17).

91.6 If the *Contractor* has instructed the *Subcontractor* to stop or not to start any substantial work or all work and an instruction allowing the work to re-start or start has not been given within fourteen weeks,

- the *Contractor* may terminate if the instruction was due to a default by the *Subcontractor* (R18),
- the *Subcontractor* may terminate if the instruction was due to a default by the *Contractor* (R19) and
- either Party may terminate if the instruction was due to any other reason (R20).

91.7 The *Contractor* may terminate if an event occurs which

- stops the *Subcontractor* completing the *subcontract works* or
- stops the *Subcontractor* completing the *subcontract works* by the date shown on the Accepted Programme and is forecast to delay Completion by more than 13 weeks,

and which

- neither Party could prevent and
- an experienced subcontractor would have judged at the Subcontract Date to have such a small chance of occurring that it would have been unreasonable for him to have allowed for it (R21).

Procedures on termination **92**

92.1 On termination, the *Contractor* may complete the *subcontract works* and may use any Plant and Materials to which he has title (P1).

92.2 The procedure on termination also includes one or more of the following as set out in the Termination Table.

P2 The *Contractor* may instruct the *Subcontractor* to leave the Site, remove any Equipment, Plant and Materials from the Site and assign the benefit of any subsubcontract or other contract related to performance of this subcontract to the *Contractor*.

P3 The *Contractor* may use any Equipment to which the *Subcontractor* has title to complete the *subcontract works*. The *Subcontractor* promptly removes the Equipment from Site when the *Contractor* notifies him that the *Contractor* no longer requires it to complete the *subcontract works*.

P4 The *Subcontractor* leaves the Working Areas and removes the Equipment.

Payment on termination **93**

93.1   The amount due on termination includes (A1)

- an amount due assessed as for normal payments,
- the Defined Cost for Plant and Materials

  - within the Working Areas or
  - to which the *Contractor* has title and of which the *Subcontractor* has to accept delivery,

- other Defined Cost reasonably incurred in expectation of completing the whole of the *subcontract works*,
- any amounts retained by the *Contractor* and
- a deduction of any un-repaid balance of an advanced payment.

93.2   The amount due on termination also includes one or more of the following as set out in the Termination Table.

A2   The forecast Defined Cost of removing the Equipment.

A3   A deduction of the forecast of the additional cost to the *Contractor* of completing the whole of the *subcontract works*.

A4   The *direct fee percentage* applied to

- for Options A, B, C and D, any excess of the total of the Prices at the Sub-contract Date over the Price for Work Done to Date or
- for Option E any excess of the first forecast of the Defined Cost for the *subcontract works* over the Price for Work Done to Date less the Fee.

MAIN OPTION CLAUSES

Option A: Priced subcontract with activity schedule

Identified and defined terms

11

11.2 (20) The Activity Schedule is the *activity schedule* unless later changed in accordance with this subcontract.

(22) Defined Cost is the cost of the components in the Shorter Schedule of Cost Components whether work is subsubcontracted or not excluding the cost of preparing quotations for compensation events.

(27) The Price for Work Done to Date is the total of the Prices for

- each group of completed activities and
- each completed activity which is not in a group.

A completed activity is one which is without Defects which would either delay or be covered by immediately following work.

(30) The Prices are the lump sum prices for each of the activities in the Activity Schedule unless later changed in accordance with this subcontract.

The programme

31

31.4 The *Subcontractor* provides information which shows how each activity on the Activity Schedule relates to the operations on each programme which he submits for acceptance.

Acceleration

36

36.3 When the *Contractor* accepts a quotation for an acceleration, he changes the Prices, the Subcontract Completion Date and the Key Dates accordingly and accepts the revised programme.

The Activity Schedule

54

54.1 Information in the Activity Schedule is not Subcontract Works Information or Site Information.

54.2 If the *Subcontractor* changes a planned method of working at his discretion so that the activities on the Activity Schedule do not relate to the operations on the Accepted Programme, he submits a revision of the Activity Schedule to the *Contractor* for acceptance.

54.3 A reason for not accepting a revision of the Activity Schedule is that

- it does not comply with the Accepted Programme,
- any changed Prices are not reasonably distributed between the activities or
- the total of the Prices is changed.

Assessing compensation events

63

63.10 If the effect of a compensation event is to reduce the total Defined Cost and the event is

- a change to the Subcontract Works Information or
- a correction of an assumption stated by the *Contractor* for assessing an earlier compensation event,

the Prices are reduced.

core clauses

main option clauses

secondary option clauses

cost components

subcontract data

63.12 Assessments for changed Prices for compensation events are in the form of changes to the Activity Schedule.

63.14 If the *Contractor* and the *Subcontractor* agree, rates and lump sums may be used to assess a compensation event.

Implementing **65**
compensation events 65.4 The changes to the Prices, the Subcontract Completion Date and the Key Dates are included in the notification implementing a compensation event.

Payment on termination **93**
93.3 The amount due on termination is assessed without taking grouping of activities into account.

Option B: Priced subcontract with bill of quantities

Identified and defined terms **11**

11.2 (21) The Bill of Quantities is the *bill of quantities* as changed in accordance with this subcontract to accommodate implemented compensation events and for accepted quotations for acceleration.

(22) Defined Cost is the cost of the components in the Shorter Schedule of Cost Components whether work is subsubcontracted or not excluding the cost of preparing quotations for compensation events.

(28) The Price for Work Done to Date is the total of

- the quantity of the work which the *Subcontractor* has completed for each item in the Bill of Quantities multiplied by the rate and
- a proportion of each lump sum which is the proportion of the work covered by the item which the *Subcontractor* has completed.

Completed work is work without Defects which would either delay or be covered by immediately following work.

(31) The Prices are the lump sums and the amounts obtained by multiplying the rates by the quantities for the items in the Bill of Quantities.

Acceleration **36**

36.3 When the *Contractor* accepts a quotation for an acceleration, he changes the Prices, the Subcontract Completion Date and the Key Dates accordingly and accepts the revised programme.

The Bill of Quantities **55**

55.1 Information in the Bill of Quantities is not Subcontract Works Information or Site Information.

Compensation events **60**

60.4 A difference between the final total quantity of work done and the quantity stated for an item in the Bill of Quantities is a compensation event if

- the difference does not result from a change to the Subcontract Works Information,
- the difference causes the Defined Cost per unit of quantity to change and
- the rate in the Bill of Quantities for the item multiplied by the final total quantity of work done is more than 0.5% of the total of the Prices at the Subcontract Date.

If the Defined Cost per unit of quantity is reduced, the affected rate is reduced.

60.5 A difference between the final total quantity of work done and the quantity for an item stated in the Bill of Quantities which delays Completion or the meeting of the Condition stated for a Key Date is a compensation event.

60.6 The *Contractor* corrects mistakes in the Bill of Quantities which are departures from the rules for item descriptions and for division of the work into items in the *method of measurement* or are due to ambiguities or inconsistencies. Each such correction is a compensation event which may lead to reduced Prices.

60.7 In assessing a compensation event which results from a correction of an inconsistency between the Bill of Quantities and another document, the *Subcontractor* is assumed to have taken the Bill of Quantities as correct.

core clauses

main option clauses

secondary option clauses

cost components

subcontract data

Assessing compensation 63
events 63.10 If the effect of a compensation event is to reduce the total Defined Cost and the event is

- a change to the Subcontract Works Information or
- a correction of an assumption stated by the *Contractor* for assessing an earlier compensation event,

the Prices are reduced.

63.13 Assessments for changed Prices for compensation events are in the form of changes to the Bill of Quantities.

- For the whole or a part of a compensation event for work not yet done and for which there is an item in the Bill of Quantities, the changes are

  - a changed rate,
  - a changed quantity or
  - a changed lump sum.

- For the whole or a part of a compensation event for work not yet done and for which there is no item in the Bill of Quantities, the change is a new priced item which, unless the *Contractor* and the *Subcontractor* agree otherwise, is compiled in accordance with the *method of measurement*.
- For the whole or a part of a compensation event for work already done, the change is a new lump sum item.

If the *Contractor* and the *Subcontractor* agree, rates and lump sums may be used to assess a compensation event.

Implementing 65
compensation events 65.4 The changes to the Prices, the Subcontract Completion Date and the Key Dates are included in the notification implementing a compensation event.

Option C: Target subcontract with activity schedule

Identified and defined	**11**	
terms	11.2	(20) The Activity Schedule is the *activity schedule* unless later changed in accordance with this subcontract.

(23) Defined Cost is

- the amount of payments due to Subsubcontractors for work which is subsubcontracted without taking account of amounts deducted for

  - retention,
  - payment to the *Contractor* as a result of a Subsubcontractor failing to meet a Key Date,
  - correction of Defects after Completion,
  - payments to Others and
  - supply of equipment, supplies and services included in the charge for overhead cost within the Working Areas in this subcontract

and

- the cost of components in the Schedule of Cost Components for other work

less Disallowed Cost.

(25) Disallowed Cost is cost which the *Contractor* decides

- is not justified by the *Subcontractor*'s accounts and records,
- should not have been paid to a Subsubcontractor or supplier in accordance with his contract,
- was incurred only because the *Subcontractor* did not

  - follow an acceptance or procurement procedure stated in the Sub-contract Works Information or
  - give an early warning which this subcontract required him to give

and the cost of

- correcting Defects after Completion,
- correcting Defects caused by the *Subcontractor* not complying with a constraint on how he is to Provide the Subcontract Works stated in the Subcontract Works Information,
- Plant and Materials not used to Provide the Subcontract Works (after allowing for reasonable wastage) unless resulting from a change to the Subcontract Works Information,
- resources not used to Provide the Subcontract Works (after allowing for reasonable availability and utilisation) or not taken away from the Working Areas when the *Contractor* requested and
- preparation for and conduct of an adjudication or proceedings of the *tribunal*.

(29) The Price for Work Done to Date is the total Defined Cost which the *Contractor* forecasts will have been paid by the *Subcontractor* before the next assessment date plus the Fee.

(30) The Prices are the lump sum prices for each of the activities in the Activity Schedule unless later changed in accordance with this subcontract.

Providing the Subcontract	**20**	
Works	20.3	The *Subcontractor* advises the *Contractor* on the practical implications of the design of the *subcontract works* and on subsubcontracting arrangements.

Sidebar: core clauses · main option clauses · secondary option clauses · cost components · subcontract data

core clauses

main option clauses

secondary option clauses

cost components

subcontract data

20.4　The *Subcontractor* prepares forecasts of the total Defined Cost for the whole of the *subcontract works* in consultation with the *Contractor* and submits them to the *Contractor*. Forecasts are prepared at the intervals stated in the Subcontract Data from the *subcontract starting date* until Completion of the whole of the *subcontract works*. An explanation of the changes made since the previous forecast is submitted with each forecast.

Subsubcontracting **26**

26.4　The *Subcontractor* submits the proposed contract data for each subsubcontract for acceptance to the *Contractor* if

- an NEC contract is proposed and
- the *Contractor* instructs the *Subcontractor* to make the submission.

A reason for not accepting the proposed contract data is that its use will not allow the *Subcontractor* to Provide the Subcontract Works.

The programme **31**

31.4　The *Subcontractor* provides information which shows how each activity on the Activity Schedule relates to the operations on each programme which he submits for acceptance.

Acceleration **36**

36.3　When the *Contractor* accepts a quotation for an acceleration, he changes the Prices, the Subcontract Completion Date and the Key Dates accordingly and accepts the revised programme.

Tests and inspections **40**

40.7　When the *Contractor* assesses the cost incurred by him in repeating a test or inspection after a Defect is found, he does not include the *Subcontractor's* cost of carrying out the repeat test or inspection.

Assessing the amount due **50**

50.6　Payments of Defined Cost made by the *Subcontractor* in a currency other than the *currency of this subcontract* are included in the amount due as payments to be made to him in the same currency. Such payments are converted to the *currency of this subcontract* in order to calculate the Fee and any *Subcontractor's* share using the *exchange rates*.

Defined Cost **52**

52.2　The *Subcontractor* keeps these records

- accounts of payments of Defined Cost,
- proof that the payments have been made,
- communications about and assessments of compensation events for Subsubcontractors and
- other records as stated in the Subcontract Works Information.

52.3　The *Subcontractor* allows the *Contractor* to inspect at any time within working hours the accounts and records which he is required to keep.

The *Subcontractor's* share **53**

53.1　The *Contractor* assesses the *Subcontractor's* share of the difference between the total of the Prices and the Price for Work Done to Date. The difference is divided into increments falling within each of the *share ranges*. The limits of a *share range* are the Price for Work Done to Date divided by the total of the Prices, expressed as a percentage. The *Subcontractor's* share equals the sum of the products of the increment within each *share range* and the corresponding *Subcontractor's* share percentage.

53.2　If the Price for Work Done to Date is less than the total of the Prices, the *Subcontractor* is paid his share of the saving. If the Price for Work Done to Date is greater than the total of the Prices, the *Subcontractor* pays his share of the excess.

53.3 The *Contractor* makes a preliminary assessment of the *Subcontractor*'s share at Completion of the whole of the *subcontract works* using his forecasts of the final Price for Work Done to Date and the final total of the Prices. This share is included in the amount due following Completion of the whole of the *subcontract works*.

53.4 The *Contractor* makes a final assessment of the *Subcontractor*'s share using the final Price for Work Done to Date and the final total of the Prices. This share is included in the final amount due.

The Activity Schedule **54**

54.1 Information in the Activity Schedule is not Subcontract Works Information or Site Information.

54.2 If the *Subcontractor* changes a planned method of working at his discretion so that the activities on the Activity Schedule do not relate to the operations on the Accepted Programme, he submits a revision of the Activity Schedule to the *Contractor* for acceptance.

54.3 A reason for not accepting a revision of the Activity Schedule is that

- it does not comply with the Accepted Programme,
- any changed Prices are not reasonably distributed between the activities or
- the total of the Prices is changed.

Assessing compensation events **63**

63.11 If the effect of a compensation event is to reduce the total Defined Cost and the event is

- a change to the Subcontract Works Information, other than a change to the Subcontract Works Information provided by the *Contractor* which the *Subcontractor* proposed and the *Contractor* has accepted or
- a correction of an assumption stated by the *Contractor* for assessing an earlier compensation event,

the Prices are reduced.

63.12 Assessments for changed Prices for compensation events are in the form of changes to the Activity Schedule.

63.14 If the *Contractor* and the *Subcontractor* agree, rates and lump sums may be used to assess a compensation event.

63.15 If the *Contractor* and the *Subcontractor* agree, the *Subcontractor* assesses a compensation event using the Shorter Schedule of Cost Components. The *Contractor* may make his own assessments using the Shorter Schedule of Cost Components.

Implementing compensation events **65**

65.4 The changes to the Prices, the Subcontract Completion Date and the Key Dates are included in the notification implementing a compensation event.

Payment on termination **93**

93.4 If there is a termination, the *Contractor* assesses the *Subcontractor*'s share after he has certified termination. His assessment uses, as the Price for Work Done to Date, the total of the Defined Cost which the *Subcontractor* has paid and which he is committed to pay for work done before termination. The assessment uses as the total of the Prices

- the lump sump price for each activity which has been completed and
- a proportion of the lump sum price for each incomplete activity which is the proportion of the work in the activity which has been completed.

93.6 The *Contractor*'s assessment of the *Subcontractor*'s share is added to the amount due to the *Subcontractor* on termination if there has been a saving or deducted if there has been an excess.

core clauses

main option clauses

secondary option clauses

cost components

subcontract data

Option D: Target subcontract with bill of quantities

core
clauses

main
option clauses

secondary
option clauses

cost
components

subcontract
data

Identified and defined 11
terms 11.2

(21) The Bill of Quantities is the *bill of quantities* as changed in accordance with this subcontract to accommodate implemented compensation events and for accepted quotations for acceleration.

(23) Defined Cost is

- the amount of payments due to Subsubcontractors for work which is subsubcontracted without taking account of amounts deducted for

  - retention,
  - payment to the *Contractor* as a result of a Subsubcontractor failing to meet a Key Date,
  - the correction of Defects after Completion,
  - payments to Others and
  - the supply of equipment, supplies and services included in the charge for overhead cost within the Working Areas in this subcontract

and

- the cost of components in the Schedule of Cost Components for other work

less Disallowed Cost.

(25) Disallowed Cost is cost which the *Contractor* decides

- is not justified by the *Subcontractor*'s accounts and records,
- should not have been paid to a Subsubcontractor or supplier in accordance with his contract,
- was incurred only because the *Subcontractor* did not

  - follow an acceptance or procurement procedure stated in the Subcontract Works Information or
  - give an early warning which this subcontract required him to give

and the cost of

- correcting Defects after Completion,
- correcting Defects caused by the *Subcontractor* not complying with a constraint on how he is to Provide the Subcontract Works stated in the Subcontract Works Information,
- Plant and Materials not used to Provide the Subcontract Works (after allowing for reasonable wastage) unless resulting from a change to the Subcontract Works Information,
- resources not used to Provide the Subcontract Works (after allowing for reasonable availability and utilisation) or not taken away from the Working Areas when the *Contractor* requested and
- preparation for and conduct of an adjudication or proceedings of the *tribunal*.

(29) The Price for Work Done to Date is the total Defined Cost which the *Contractor* forecasts will have been paid by the *Subcontractor* before the next assessment date plus the Fee.

(31) The Prices are the lump sums and the amounts obtained by multiplying the rates by the quantities for the items in the Bill of Quantities.

(33) The Total of the Prices is the total of

- the quantity of the work which the *Subcontractor* has completed for each item in the Bill of Quantities multiplied by the rate and
- a proportion of each lump sum which is the proportion of the work covered by the item which the *Subcontractor* has completed.

Completed work is work without Defects which would either delay or be covered by immediately following work.

Providing the Subcontract Works **20**

20.3 The *Subcontractor* advises the *Contractor* on the practical implications of the design of the *subcontract works* and on subsubcontracting arrangements.

20.4 The *Subcontractor* prepares forecasts of the total Defined Cost for the whole of the *subcontract works* in consultation with the *Contractor* and submits them to the *Contractor*. Forecasts are prepared at the intervals stated in the Subcontract Data from the *subcontract starting date* until Completion of the whole of the *subcontract works*. An explanation of the changes made since the previous forecast is submitted with each forecast.

Subsubcontracting **26**

26.4 The *Subcontractor* submits the proposed contract data for each subsubcontract for acceptance to the *Contractor* if

- an NEC contract is proposed and
- the *Contractor* instructs the *Subcontractor* to make the submission.

A reason for not accepting the proposed contract data is that its use will not allow the *Subcontractor* to Provide the Subcontract Works.

Acceleration **36**

36.3 When the *Contractor* accepts a quotation for an acceleration, he changes the Prices, the Subcontract Completion Date and the Key Dates accordingly and accepts the revised programme.

Tests and inspections **40**

40.7 When the *Contractor* assesses the cost incurred by him in repeating a test or inspection after a Defect is found, he does not include the *Subcontractor*'s cost of carrying out the repeat test or inspection.

Assessing the amount due **50**

50.6 Payments of Defined Cost made by the *Subcontractor* in a currency other than the *currency of this subcontract* are included in the amount due as payments to be made to him in the same currency. Such payments are converted to the *currency of this subcontract* in order to calculate the Fee and any *Subcontractor*'s share using the *exchange rates*.

Defined Cost **52**

52.2 The *Subcontractor* keeps these records

- accounts of payments of Defined Cost,
- proof that the payments have been made,
- communications about and assessments of compensation events for Subsubcontractors and
- other records as stated in the Subcontract Works Information.

52.3 The *Subcontractor* allows the *Contractor* to inspect at any time within working hours the accounts and records which he is required to keep.

core clauses

main option clauses

secondary option clauses

cost components

subcontract data

The *Subcontractor*'s share **53**

53.5 The *Contractor* assesses the *Subcontractor*'s share of the difference between the Total of the Prices and the Price for Work Done to Date. The difference is divided into increments falling within each of the *share ranges*. The limits of a *share range* are the Price for Work Done to Date divided by the Total of the Prices, expressed as a percentage. The *Subcontractor*'s share equals the sum of the products of the increment within each *share range* and the corresponding *Subcontractor's share percentage.*

53.6 If the Price for Work Done to Date is less than the Total of the Prices, the *Subcontractor* is paid his share of the saving. If the Price for Work Done to Date is greater than the Total of the Prices, the *Subcontractor* pays his share of the excess.

53.7 The *Contractor* makes a preliminary assessment of the *Subcontractor*'s share at Completion of the whole of the *subcontract works* using his forecasts of the final Price for Work Done to Date and the final Total of the Prices. This share is included in the amount due following Completion of the whole of the *subcontract works*.

53.8 The *Contractor* makes a final assessment of the *Subcontractor*'s share using the final Price for Work Done to Date and the final Total of the Prices. This share is included in the final amount due.

The Bill of Quantities **55**

55.1 Information in the Bill of Quantities is not Subcontract Works Information or Site Information.

Compensation events **60**

60.4 A difference between the final total quantity of work done and the quantity stated for an item in the Bill of Quantities is a compensation event if

- the difference does not result from a change to the Subcontract Works Information,
- the difference causes the Defined Cost per unit of quantity to change and
- the rate in the Bill of Quantities for the item multiplied by the final total quantity of work done is more than 0.5% of the total of the Prices at the Subcontract Date.

If the Defined Cost per unit of quantity is reduced, the affected rate is reduced.

60.5 A difference between the final total quantity of work done and the quantity for an item stated in the Bill of Quantities which delays Completion or the meeting of the Condition stated for a Key Date is a compensation event.

60.6 The *Contractor* corrects mistakes in the Bill of Quantities which are departures from the rules for item descriptions and for division of the work into items in the *method of measurement* or are due to ambiguities or inconsistencies. Each such correction is a compensation event which may lead to reduced Prices.

60.7 In assessing a compensation event which results from a correction of an inconsistency between the Bill of Quantities and another document, the *Subcontractor* is assumed to have taken the Bill of Quantities as correct.

Assessing compensation events **63**

63.11 If the effect of a compensation event is to reduce the total Defined Cost and the event is

- a change to the Subcontract Works Information, other than a change to the Subcontract Works Information provided by the *Contractor* which the *Subcontractor* proposed and the *Contractor* has accepted or
- a correction of an assumption stated by the *Contractor* for assessing an earlier compensation event,

the Prices are reduced.

63.13 Assessments for changed Prices for compensation events are in the form of changes to the Bill of Quantities.

- For the whole or a part of a compensation event for work not yet done and for which there is an item in the Bill of Quantities, the changes are

  - a changed rate,
  - a changed quantity or
  - a changed lump sum.

- For the whole or a part of a compensation event for work not yet done and for which there is no item in the Bill of Quantities, the change is a new priced item which, unless the *Contractor* and the *Subcontractor* agree otherwise, is compiled in accordance with the *method of measurement*.
- For the whole or a part of a compensation event for work already done, the change is a new lump sum item.

If the *Contractor* and the *Subcontractor* agree, rates and lump sums may be used to assess a compensation event.

63.15 If the *Contractor* and the *Subcontractor* agree, the *Subcontractor* assesses a compensation event using the Shorter Schedule of Cost Components. The *Contractor* may make his own assessments using the Shorter Schedule of Cost Components.

Implementing compensation events **65**

65.4 The changes to the Prices, the Subcontract Completion Date and the Key Dates are included in the notification implementing a compensation event.

Payment on termination **93**

93.5 If there is a termination, the *Contractor* assesses the *Subcontractor*'s share after he has certified termination. His assessment uses, as the Price for Work Done to Date, the total of the Defined Cost which the *Subcontractor* has paid and which he is committed to pay for work done before termination.

93.6 The *Contractor*'s assessment of the *Subcontractor*'s share is added to the amount due to the *Subcontractor* on termination if there has been a saving or deducted if there has been an excess.

core clauses

main option clauses

secondary option clauses

cost components

subcontract data

Option E: Cost reimbursable subcontract

core clauses

main option clauses

secondary option clauses

cost components

subcontract data

Identified and defined **11**
terms 11.2 (23) Defined Cost is

- the amount of payments due to Subsubcontractors for work which is subsubcontracted without taking account of amounts deducted for
  - retention,
  - payment to the *Contractor* as a result of a Subsubcontractor failing to meet a Key Date,
  - the correction of Defects after Completion,
  - payments to Others and
  - the supply of equipment, supplies and services included in the charge for overhead cost within the Working Areas in this subcontract

and

- the cost of components in the Schedule of Cost Components for other work

less Disallowed Cost.

(25) Disallowed Cost is cost which the *Contractor* decides

- is not justified by the *Subcontractor*'s accounts and records,
- should not have been paid to a Subsubcontractor or supplier in accordance with his contract,
- was incurred only because the *Subcontractor* did not
  - follow an acceptance or procurement procedure stated in the Subcontract Works Information or
  - give an early warning which this subcontract required him to give

and the cost of

- correcting Defects after Completion,
- correcting Defects caused by the *Subcontractor* not complying with a constraint on how he is to Provide the Subcontract Works stated in the Subcontract Works Information,
- Plant and Materials not used to Provide the Subcontract Works (after allowing for reasonable wastage) unless resulting from a change to the Subcontract Works Information,
- resources not used to Provide the Subcontract Works (after allowing for reasonable availability and utilisation) or not taken away from the Working Areas when the *Contractor* requested and
- preparation for and conduct of an adjudication or proceedings of the *tribunal*.

(29) The Price for Work Done to Date is the total Defined Cost which the *Contractor* forecasts will have been paid by the *Subcontractor* before the next assessment date plus the Fee.

(32) The Prices are the Defined Cost plus the Fee.

Providing the Subcontract **20**
Works

20.3 The *Subcontractor* advises the *Contractor* on the practical implications of the design of the *subcontract works* and on subsubcontracting arrangements.

20.4 The *Subcontractor* prepares forecasts of the total Defined Cost for the whole of the *subcontract works* in consultation with the *Contractor* and submits them to the *Contractor*. Forecasts are prepared at the intervals stated in the Subcontract Data from the *subcontract starting date* until Completion of the whole of the *subcontract works*. An explanation of the changes made since the previous forecast is submitted with each forecast.

Subsubcontracting **26**

26.4 The *Subcontractor* submits the proposed contract data for each subsubcontract for acceptance to the *Contractor* if

- an NEC contract is proposed and
- the *Contractor* instructs the *Subcontractor* to make the submission.

A reason for not accepting the proposed contract data is that its use will not allow the *Subcontractor* to Provide the Subcontract Works.

Acceleration **36**

36.4 When the *Contractor* accepts a quotation for an acceleration, he changes the Subcontract Completion Date, the Key Dates and the forecast of the total Defined Cost of the whole of the *subcontract works* accordingly and accepts the revised programme.

Tests and inspections **40**

40.7 When the *Contractor* assesses the cost incurred by him in repeating a test or inspection after a Defect is found, he does not include the *Subcontractor*'s cost of carrying out the repeat test or inspection.

Assessing the amount due **50**

50.7 Payments of Defined Cost made by the *Subcontractor* in a currency other than the *currency of this subcontract* are included in the amount due as payments to be made to him in the same currency. Such payments are converted to the *currency of this subcontract* in order to calculate the Fee using the *exchange rates*.

Defined Cost **52**

52.2 The *Subcontractor* keeps these records

- accounts of payments of Defined Cost,
- proof that the payments have been made,
- communications about and assessments of compensation events for Subsubcontractors and
- other records as stated in the Subcontract Works Information.

52.3 The *Subcontractor* allows the *Contractor* to inspect at any time within working hours the accounts and records which he is required to keep.

Assessing compensation events **63**

63.14 If the *Contractor* and the *Subcontractor* agree, rates and lump sums may be used to assess a compensation event.

63.15 If the *Contractor* and the *Subcontractor* agree, the *Subcontractor* assesses a compensation event using the Shorter Schedule of Cost Components. The *Contractor* may make his own assessments using the Shorter Schedule of Cost Components.

Implementing compensation events **65**

65.3 The changes to the forecast amount of the Prices, the Subcontract Completion Date and the Key Dates are included in the notification implementing a compensation event.

core clauses

main option clauses

secondary option clauses

cost components

subcontract data

DISPUTE RESOLUTION

Option W1

Dispute resolution procedure (used unless the United Kingdom Housing Grants, Construction and Regeneration Act 1996 applies).

core clauses

main option clauses

secondary option clauses

cost components

subcontract data

Dispute resolution **W1**

W1.1 A dispute arising under or in connection with this subcontract is referred to and decided by the *Adjudicator*.

The *Adjudicator* W1.2 (1) The Parties appoint the *Adjudicator* under the NEC Adjudicator's Contract current at the *subcontract starting date*.

(2) The *Adjudicator* acts impartially and decides the dispute as an independent adjudicator and not as an arbitrator.

(3) If the *Adjudicator* is not identified in the Subcontract Data or if the *Adjudicator* resigns or is unable to act, the Parties choose a new adjudicator jointly. If the Parties have not chosen an adjudicator, either Party may ask the *Adjudicator nominating body* to choose one. The *Adjudicator nominating body* chooses an adjudicator within four days of the request. The chosen adjudicator becomes the *Adjudicator*.

(4) A replacement *Adjudicator* has the power to decide a dispute referred to his predecessor but not decided at the time when the predecessor resigned or became unable to act. He deals with an undecided dispute as if it had been referred to him on the date he was appointed.

(5) The *Adjudicator*, his employees and agents are not liable to the Parties for any action or failure to take action in an adjudication unless the action or failure to take action was in bad faith.

The adjudication W1.3 (1) Disputes are notified and referred to the *Adjudicator* in accordance with the Adjudication Table.

ADJUDICATION TABLE

Dispute about	Which Party may refer it to the *Adjudicator*?	When may it be referred to the *Adjudicator*?
An action of the *Contractor*	The *Subcontractor*	Between two and four weeks after the *Subcontractor*'s notification of the dispute to the *Contractor*, the notification itself being made not more than four weeks after the *Subcontractor* becomes aware of the action
The *Contractor* not having taken an action	The *Subcontractor*	Between two and four weeks after the *Subcontractor*'s notification of the dispute to the *Contractor*, the notification itself being made not more than four weeks after the *Subcontractor* becomes aware that the action was not taken
A quotation for a compensation event which is treated as having been accepted	The *Contractor*	Between two and four weeks after the *Contractor*'s notification of the dispute to the *Subcontractor,* the notification itself being made not more than four weeks after the quotation was treated as accepted
Any other matter	Either Party	Between two and four weeks after notification of the dispute to the other Party

(2) The times for notifying and referring a dispute may be extended by the *Contractor* if the *Subcontractor* and the *Contractor* agree to the extension before the notice or referral is due. The *Contractor* notifies the extension that has been agreed to the *Subcontractor*. If a disputed matter is not notified and referred within the times set out in this subcontract, neither Party may subsequently refer it to the *Adjudicator* or the *tribunal*.

(3) The Party referring the dispute to the *Adjudicator* includes with his referral information to be considered by the *Adjudicator*. Any more information from a Party to be considered by the *Adjudicator* is provided within four weeks of the referral. This period may be extended if the *Adjudicator* and the Parties agree.

(4a) If a matter disputed by the *Subcontractor* under or in connection with a subsubcontract is also a matter disputed under or in connection with this subcontract and if the subsubcontract allows, the *Subcontractor* may refer the subsubcontract dispute to the *Adjudicator* at the same time as the subcontract referral. The *Adjudicator* then decides the disputes together and references to the Parties for the purposes of the dispute are interpreted as including the Subsubcontractor.

(4b) Within two weeks of the notification of the dispute by the *Subcontractor* to the *Contractor*, the *Contractor* notifies the *Subcontractor* if the matter disputed is a matter disputed under or in connection with the main contract.

The *Contractor* may then

- submit the subcontract dispute to the *main contract Adjudicator* at the same time as the main contract submission and
- instruct the *Subcontractor* to provide any information which the *Contractor* may require.

The *main contract Adjudicator* then decides the disputes together.

(5) The *Adjudicator* may

- review and revise any action or inaction of the *Contractor* related to the dispute and alter a quotation which has been treated as having been accepted,
- take the initiative in ascertaining the facts and the law related to the dispute,
- instruct a Party to provide further information related to the dispute within a stated time and
- instruct a Party to take any other action which he considers necessary to reach his decision and to do so within a stated time.

(6) A communication between a Party and the *Adjudicator* is communicated to the other Party at the same time.

(7) If the *Adjudicator*'s decision includes assessment of additional cost or delay caused to the *Subcontractor*, he makes his assessment in the same way as a compensation event is assessed.

(8) The *Adjudicator* decides the dispute and notifies the Parties of his decision and his reasons within four weeks of the end of the period for receiving information. This four week period may be extended if the Parties agree.

(9) Unless and until the *Adjudicator* has notified the Parties of his decision, the Parties, the *Contractor* and the *Subcontractor* proceed as if the matter disputed was not disputed.

(10) The *Adjudicator*'s decision is binding on the Parties unless and until revised by the *tribunal* and is enforceable as a matter of contractual obligation between the Parties and not as an arbitral award. The *Adjudicator*'s decision is final and binding if neither Party has notified the other within the times required by this subcontract that he is dissatisfied with a decision of the *Adjudicator* and intends to refer the matter to the *tribunal*.

(11) The *Adjudicator* may, within two weeks of giving his decision to the Parties, correct any clerical mistake or ambiguity.

Review by the *tribunal* W1.4 (1) A Party does not refer any dispute under or in connection with this subcontract to the *tribunal* unless it has first been referred to the *Adjudicator* in accordance with this subcontract.

(2) If, after the *Adjudicator* notifies his decision a Party is dissatisfied, he may notify the other Party that he intends to refer it to the *tribunal*. A Party may not refer a dispute to the *tribunal* unless this notification is given within four weeks of notification of the *Adjudicator*'s decision.

(3) If the *Adjudicator* does not notify his decision within the time provided by this subcontract, a Party may notify the other Party that he intends to refer the dispute to the *tribunal*. A Party may not refer a dispute to the *tribunal* unless this notification is given within four weeks of the date by which the *Adjudicator* should have notified his decision.

(4) The *tribunal* settles the dispute referred to it. The *tribunal* has the powers to reconsider any decision of the *Adjudicator* and review and revise any action or inaction of the *Contractor* related to the dispute. A Party is not limited in the *tribunal* proceedings to the information, evidence or arguments put to the *Adjudicator*.

(5) If the *tribunal* is arbitration, the *arbitration procedure*, the place where the arbitration is to be held and the method of choosing the arbitrator are those stated in the Subcontract Data.

(6) A Party does not call the *Adjudicator* as a witness in *tribunal* proceedings.

Option W2

Dispute resolution procedure (used in the United Kingdom when the Housing Grants, Construction and Regeneration Act 1996 applies).

Dispute resolution	**W2**	
	W2.1	(1) Any dispute arising under or in connection with this subcontract is referred to and decided by the *Adjudicator*. A Party may refer a dispute to the *Adjudicator* at any time.

(2) In this Option, time periods stated in days exclude Christmas Day, Good Friday and bank holidays.

The *Adjudicator*   W2.2   (1) The Parties appoint the *Adjudicator* under the NEC Adjudicator's Contract current at the *subcontract starting date*.

(2) The *Adjudicator* acts impartially and decides the dispute as an independent adjudicator and not as an arbitrator.

(3) If the *Adjudicator* is not identified in the Subcontract Data or if the *Adjudicator* resigns or becomes unable to act

- the Parties may choose an adjudicator jointly or
- a Party may ask the *Adjudicator nominating body* to choose an adjudicator.

The *Adjudicator nominating body* chooses an adjudicator within four days of the request. The chosen adjudicator becomes the *Adjudicator*.

(4) A replacement *Adjudicator* has the power to decide a dispute referred to his predecessor but not decided at the time when his predecessor resigned or became unable to act. He deals with an undecided dispute as if it had been referred to him on the date he was appointed.

(5) The *Adjudicator,* his employees and agents are not liable to the Parties for any action or failure to take action in an adjudication unless the action or failure to take action was in bad faith.

The adjudication   W2.3   (1) Before a Party refers a dispute to the *Adjudicator*, he gives a notice of adjudication to the other Party with a brief description of the dispute and the decision which he wishes the *Adjudicator* to make. If the *Adjudicator* is named in the Subcontract Data, the Party sends a copy of the notice of adjudication to the *Adjudicator* when it is issued. Within three days of the receipt of the notice of adjudication, the *Adjudicator* notifies the Parties

- that he is able to decide the dispute in accordance with the subcontract or
- that he is unable to decide the dispute and has resigned.

If the *Adjudicator* does not so notify within three days of the issue of the notice of adjudication, either Party may act as if he has resigned.

(2) Within seven days of a Party giving a notice of adjudication he

- refers the dispute to the *Adjudicator*,
- provides the *Adjudicator* with the information on which he relies, including any supporting documents and
- provides a copy of the information and supporting documents he has provided to the *Adjudicator* to the other Party.

Any further information from a Party to be considered by the *Adjudicator* is provided within fourteen days of the referral. This period may be extended if the *Adjudicator* and the Parties agree.

core clauses

main option clauses

secondary option clauses

cost components

subcontract data

(3a) If a matter disputed by the *Subcontractor* under or in connection with a subsubcontract is also a matter disputed under or in connection with this subcontract, the *Subcontractor* may, with the consent of the Subsubcontractor, refer the subsubcontract dispute to the *Adjudicator* at the same time as the subcontract referral. The *Adjudicator* then decides the disputes together and references to the Parties for the purposes of the dispute are interpreted as including the Subsubcontractor.

(3b) Within two weeks of the notification of the dispute by the *Subcontractor* to the *Contractor*, the *Contractor* notifies the *Subcontractor* if the matter disputed is a matter disputed under or in connection with the main contract.

The *Contractor* may, with the consent of the *Subcontractor*, then

- submit the subcontract dispute to the *main contract Adjudicator* at the same time as the main contract submission and
- instruct the *Subcontractor* to provide any information which the *Contractor* may require.

The *main contract Adjudicator* then settles the two disputes together.

(4) The *Adjudicator* may

- review and revise any action or inaction of the *Contractor* related to the dispute and alter a quotation which has been treated as having been accepted,
- take the initiative in ascertaining the facts and the law related to the dispute,
- instruct a Party to provide further information related to the dispute within a stated time and
- instruct a Party to take any other action which he considers necessary to reach his decision and to do so within a stated time.

(5) If a Party does not comply with any instruction within the time stated by the *Adjudicator,* the *Adjudicator* may continue the adjudication and make his decision based upon the information and evidence he has received.

(6) A communication between a Party and the *Adjudicator* is communicated to the other Party at the same time.

(7) If the *Adjudicator*'s decision includes assessment of additional cost or delay caused to the *Subcontractor,* he makes his assessment in the same way as a compensation event is assessed. If the *Adjudicator*'s decision changes an amount notified as due, payment of the sum decided by the *Adjudicator* is due not later than seven days from the date of the decision or the final date for payment of the notified amount, whichever is the later.

(8) The *Adjudicator* decides the dispute and notifies the Parties of his decision and his reasons within twenty-eight days of the dispute being referred to him. This period may be extended by up to fourteen days with the consent of the referring Party or by any other period agreed by the Parties. The *Adjudicator* may in his decision allocate his fees and expenses between the Parties.

(9) Unless and until the *Adjudicator* has notified the Parties of his decision, the Parties proceed as if the matter disputed was not disputed.

(10) If the *Adjudicator* does not make his decision and notify it to the Parties within the time provided by this subcontract, the Parties and the *Adjudicator* may agree to extend the period for making his decision. If they do not agree to an extension, either Party may act as if the *Adjudicator* has resigned.

(11) The *Adjudicator*'s decision is binding on the Parties unless and until revised by the *tribunal* and is enforceable as a matter of contractual obligation between the Parties and not as an arbitral award. The *Adjudicator*'s decision is final and binding if neither Party has notified the other within the times required by this subcontract that he is dissatisfied with a matter decided by the *Adjudicator* and intends to refer the matter to the *tribunal*.

(12) The *Adjudicator* may, within five days of giving his decision to the Parties, correct the decision to remove a clerical or typographical error arising by accident or omission.

Review by the *tribunal* W2.4 (1) A Party does not refer any dispute under or in connection with this sub-contract to the *tribunal* unless it has first been decided by the *Adjudicator* in accordance with this subcontract.

(2) If, after the *Adjudicator* notifies his decision a Party is dissatisfied, that Party may notify the other Party of the matter which he disputes and state that he intends to refer it to the *tribunal*. The dispute may not be referred to the *tribunal* unless this notification is given within four weeks of the notification of the *Adjudicator's* decision.

(3) The *tribunal* settles the dispute referred to it. The *tribunal* has the powers to reconsider any decision of the *Adjudicator* and to review and revise any action or inaction of the *Contractor* related to the dispute. A Party is not limited in *tribunal* proceedings to the information or evidence put to the *Adjudicator*.

(4) If the *tribunal* is arbitration, the *arbitration procedure,* the place where the arbitration is to be held and the method of choosing the arbitrator are those stated in the Subcontract Data.

(5) A Party does not call the *Adjudicator* as a witness in *tribunal* proceedings.

core
clauses

main
option clauses

secondary
option clauses

cost
components

subcontract
data

SECONDARY OPTION CLAUSES

Option X1: Price adjustment for inflation (used only with Options A, B, C and D)

Defined terms	**X1**	
	X1.1	(a) The Base Date Index (B) is the latest available index before the *base date*.

(b) The Latest Index (L) is the latest available index before the date of assessment of an amount due.

(c) The Price Adjustment Factor is the total of the products of each of the proportions stated in the Subcontract Data multiplied by $(L - B)/B$ for the index linked to it.

Price Adjustment Factor X1.2 If an index is changed after it has been used in calculating a Price Adjustment Factor, the calculation is repeated and a correction included in the next assessment of the amount due.

The Price Adjustment Factor calculated at the Subcontract Completion Date for the whole of the *subcontract works* is used for calculating price adjustment after this date.

Compensation events X1.3 The Defined Cost for compensation events is assessed using the

- Defined Cost current at the time of assessing the compensation event adjusted to *base date* by dividing by one plus the Price Adjustment Factor for the last assessment of the amount due and
- Defined Cost at *base date* levels for amounts calculated from rates stated in the Subcontract Data for employees and Equipment.

Price adjustment Options A and B X1.4 Each amount due includes an amount for price adjustment which is the sum of

- the change in the Price for Work Done to Date since the last assessment of the amount due multiplied by the Price Adjustment Factor for the date of the current assessment,
- the amount for price adjustment included in the previous amount due and
- correcting amounts, not included elsewhere, which arise from changes to indices used for assessing previous amounts for price adjustment.

Price adjustment Options C and D X1.5 Each time the amount due is assessed, an amount for price adjustment is added to the total of the Prices which is the sum of

- the change in the Price for Work Done to Date since the last assessment of the amount due multiplied by $(PAF/(1+PAF))$ where PAF is the Price Adjustment Factor for the date of the current assessment and
- correcting amounts, not included elsewhere, which arise from changes to indices used for assessing previous amounts for price adjustment.

Option X2: Changes in the law

Changes in the law **X2**

X2.1   A change in the law of the country in which the Site is located is a compensation event if it occurs after the Subcontract Date. The *Contractor* may notify the *Subcontractor* of a compensation event for a change in the law and instruct him to submit quotations. If the effect of a compensation event which is a change in the law is to reduce the total Defined Cost, the Prices are reduced.

Option X3: Multiple currencies (used only with Options A and B)

Multiple currencies **X3**

X3.1   The *Subcontractor* is paid in currencies other than the *currency of this subcontract* for the items or activities listed in the Subcontract Data. The *exchange rates* are used to convert from the *currency of this subcontract* to other currencies.

X3.2   Payments to the *Subcontractor* in currencies other than the *currency of this subcontract* do not exceed the maximum amounts stated in the Subcontract Data. Any excess is paid in the *currency of this subcontract*.

Option X4: Parent company guarantee

Parent company **X4**
guarantee X4.1   If a parent company owns the *Subcontractor*, the *Subcontractor* gives to the *Contractor* a guarantee by the parent company of the *Subcontractor*'s performance in the form set out in the Subcontract Works Information. If the guarantee was not given by the Subcontract Date, it is given to the *Contractor* within four weeks of the Subcontract Date.

Option X5: Sectional Completion

Sectional Completion **X5**

X5.1   In these *conditions of subcontract*, unless stated as the whole of the *subcontract works*, each reference and clause relevant to

- the *subcontract works*,
- Completion and
- Subcontract Completion Date

applies, as the case may be, to either the whole of the *subcontract works* or any *section* of the *subcontract works*.

core clauses

main option clauses

secondary option clauses

cost components

subcontract data

Option X6: Bonus for early Completion

Bonus for early Completion **X6**

X6.1 The *Subcontractor* is paid a bonus calculated at the rate stated in the Subcontract Data for each day from the earlier of

- Completion and
- the date on which the *Contractor* takes over the *subcontract works*

until the Subcontract Completion Date.

Option X7: Delay damages

Delay damages **X7**

X7.1 The *Subcontractor* pays delay damages at the rate stated in the Subcontract Data from the Subcontract Completion Date for each day until the earlier of

- Completion and
- the date on which the *Contractor* takes over the *subcontract works*.

X7.2 If the Subcontract Completion Date is changed to a later date after delay damages have been paid, the *Contractor* repays the overpayment of damages with interest. Interest is assessed from the date of payment to the date of repayment and the date of repayment is an assessment date.

X7.3 If the *Contractor* takes over a part of the *subcontract works* before Completion, the delay damages are reduced from the date on which the part is taken over. The *Contractor* assesses the benefit of taking over the part of the *subcontract works* as a proportion of the benefit of taking over the whole of the *subcontract works* not previously taken over. The delay damages are reduced in this proportion.

Option X12: Partnering

Identified and defined **X12**
terms X12.1 (1) The Partners are those named in the Schedule of Partners. The *Client* is a Partner.

(2) An Own Contract is a contract between two Partners which includes this Option.

(3) The Core Group comprises the Partners listed in the Schedule of Core Group Members.

(4) Partnering Information is information which specifies how the Partners work together and is either in the documents which the Subcontract Data states it is in or in an instruction given in accordance with this subcontract.

(5) A Key Performance Indicator is an aspect of performance for which a target is stated in the Schedule of Partners.

Actions X12.2 (1) Each Partner works with the other Partners to achieve the *Client*'s *objective* stated in the Subcontract Data and the objectives of every other Partner stated in the Schedule of Partners.

(2) Each Partner nominates a representative to act for it in dealings with other Partners.

(3) The Core Group acts and takes decisions on behalf of the Partners on those matters stated in the Partnering Information.

(4) The Partners select the members of the Core Group. The Core Group decides how they will work and decides the dates when each member joins and leaves the Core Group. The *Client*'s representative leads the Core Group unless stated otherwise in the Partnering Information.

(5) The Core Group keeps the Schedule of Core Group Members and the Schedule of Partners up to date and issues copies of them to the Partners each time either is revised.

(6) This Option does not create a legal partnership between Partners who are not one of the Parties in this subcontract.

Working together X12.3 (1) The Partners work together as stated in the Partnering Information and in a spirit of mutual trust and co-operation.

(2) A Partner may ask another Partner to provide information which he needs to carry out the work in his Own Contract and the other Partner provides it.

(3) Each Partner gives an early warning to the other Partners when he becomes aware of any matter that could affect the achievement of another Partner's objectives stated in the Schedule of Partners.

(4) The Partners use common information systems as set out in the Partnering Information.

(5) A Partner implements a decision of the Core Group by issuing instructions in accordance with its Own Contracts.

(6) The Core Group may give an instruction to the Partners to change the Partnering Information. Each such change to the Partnering Information is a compensation event which may lead to reduced Prices.

(7) The Core Group prepares and maintains a timetable showing the proposed timing of the contributions of the Partners. The Core Group issues a copy of the timetable to the Partners each time it is revised. The *Subcontractor* changes his programme if it is necessary to do so in order to comply with the revised timetable. Each such change is a compensation event which may lead to reduced Prices.

(8) A Partner gives advice, information and opinion to the Core Group and to other Partners when asked to do so by the Core Group. This advice, information and opinion relates to work that another Partner is to carry out under its Own Contract and is given fully, openly and objectively. The Partners show contingency and risk allowances in information about costs, prices and timing for future work.

(9) A Partner notifies the Core Group before subsubcontracting any work.

Incentives X12.4 (1) A Partner is paid the amount stated in the Schedule of Partners if the target stated for a Key Performance Indicator is improved upon or achieved. Payment of the amount is due when the target has been improved upon or achieved and is made as part of the amount due in the Partner's Own Contract.

(2) The *Client* may add a Key Performance Indicator and associated payment to the Schedule of Partners but may not delete or reduce a payment stated in the Schedule of Partners.

core clauses

main option clauses

secondary option clauses

cost components

subcontract data

Option X13: Performance bond

Performance bond **X13**

X13.1 The *Subcontractor* gives the *Contractor* a performance bond, provided by a bank or insurer which the *Contractor* has accepted, for the amount stated in the Subcontract Data and in the form set out in the Subcontract Works Information. A reason for not accepting the bank or insurer is that its commercial position is not strong enough to carry the bond. If the bond was not given by the Subcontract Date, it is given to the *Contractor* within four weeks of the Subcontract Date.

Option X14: Advanced payment to the *Subcontractor*

Advanced payment **X14**

X14.1 The *Contractor* makes an advanced payment to the *Subcontractor* of the amount stated in the Subcontract Data.

X14.2 The advanced payment is made either within five weeks of the Subcontract Date or, if an advanced payment bond is required, within five weeks of the later of

- the Subcontract Date and
- the date when the *Contractor* receives the advanced payment bond.

The advanced payment bond is issued by a bank or insurer which the *Contractor* has accepted. A reason for not accepting the proposed bank or insurer is that its commercial position is not strong enough to carry the bond. The bond is for the amount of the advanced payment which the *Subcontractor* has not repaid and is in the form set out in the Subcontract Works Information. Delay in making the advanced payment is a compensation event.

X14.3 The advanced payment is repaid to the *Contractor* by the *Subcontractor* in instalments of the amount stated in the Subcontract Data. An instalment is included in each amount due assessed after the period stated in the Subcontract Data has passed until the advanced payment has been repaid.

Option X15: Limitation of the *Subcontractor*'s liability for his design to reasonable skill and care

The *Subcontractor*'s design **X15**

X15.1 The *Subcontractor* is not liable for Defects in the *subcontract works* due to his design so far as he proves that he used reasonable skill and care to ensure that his design complied with the Subcontract Works Information.

X15.2 If the *Subcontractor* corrects a Defect for which he is not liable under this subcontract it is a compensation event.

Option X16: Retention

Retention **X16**

X16.1 After the Price for Work Done to Date has reached the *retention free amount*, an amount is retained in each amount due. Until the earlier of

- Completion of the whole of the *subcontract works* and
- the date on which the *Contractor* takes over the whole of the *subcontract works*

the amount retained is the *retention percentage* applied to the excess of the Price for Work Done to Date above the *retention free amount*.

X16.2 The amount retained is halved

- in the assessment made at Completion of the whole of the *subcontract works* or
- in the next assessment after the *Contractor* has taken over the whole of the *subcontract works* if this is before Completion of the whole of the *subcontract works*.

The amount retained remains at this amount until the Defects Certificate is issued. No amount is retained in the assessments made after the Defects Certificate has been issued.

Option X17: Low performance damages

Low performance **X17**
damages X17.1 If a Defect included in the Defects Certificate shows low performance with respect to a performance level stated in the Subcontract Data, the *Subcontractor* pays the amount of low performance damages stated in the Subcontract Data.

Option X18: Limitation of liability

Limitation of liability **X18**

X18.1 The *Subcontractor*'s liability to the *Contractor* for the *Contractor*'s indirect or consequential loss is limited to the amount stated in the Subcontract Data.

X18.2 For any one event, the liability of the *Subcontractor* to the *Contractor* for loss of or damage to the *Employer*'s or *Contractor*'s property is limited to the amount stated in the Subcontract Data.

X18.3 The *Subcontractor*'s liability to the *Contractor* for Defects due to his design which are not listed on the Defects Certificate is limited to the amount stated in the Subcontract Data.

X18.4 The *Subcontractor*'s total liability to the *Contractor* for all matters arising under or in connection with this subcontract, other than the excluded matters, is limited to the amount stated in the Subcontract Data and applies in contract, tort or delict and otherwise to the extent allowed under the *law of the subcontract*.

The excluded matters are amounts payable by the *Subcontractor* as stated in this subcontract for

- loss of or damage to the *Employer*'s or the *Contractor*'s property,
- delay damages if Option X7 applies,
- low performance damages if Option X17 applies and
- *Subcontractor*'s share if Option C or Option D applies.

core clauses

main option clauses

secondary option clauses

cost components

subcontract data

X18.5   The *Subcontractor* is not liable to the *Contractor* for a matter unless it is notified to the *Subcontractor* before the *end of liability date*.

Option X20: Key Performance Indicators (not used with Option X12)

Incentives   X20.1   A Key Performance Indicator is an aspect of performance by the *Subcontractor* for which a target is stated in the Incentive Schedule. The Incentive Schedule is the *incentive schedule* unless later changed in accordance with this subcontract.

X20.2   From the *subcontract starting date* until the Defects Certificate has been issued, the *Subcontractor* reports to the *Contractor* his performance against each of the Key Performance Indicators. Reports are provided at the intervals stated in the Subcontract Data and include the forecast final measurement against each indicator.

X20.3   If the *Subcontractor*'s forecast final measurement against a Key Performance Indicator will not achieve the target stated in the Incentive Schedule, he submits to the *Contractor* his proposals for improving performance.

X20.4   The *Subcontractor* is paid the amount stated in the Incentive Schedule if the target stated for a Key Performance Indicator is improved upon or achieved. Payment of the amount is due when the target has been improved upon or achieved.

X20.5   The *Contractor* may add a Key Performance Indicator and associated payment to the Incentive Schedule but may not delete or reduce a payment stated in the Incentive Schedule.

OPTION Y

Option Y(UK)1: Project Bank Account

Definitions **Y(UK)1**

Y1.1 (1) The Authorisation is a document authorising the *project bank* to make payments to the *Contractor*, the *Subcontractor* and Subcontract Named Suppliers.

(2) Subcontract Named Suppliers are *named suppliers* and other Suppliers who have signed the Joining Deed.

(3) Project Bank Account is the account established by the *Contractor* and used to make payments to the *Subcontractor* and Subcontract Named Suppliers.

(4) A Supplier is a person or organisation who has a contract to

- construct or install part of the *subcontract works,*
- provide a service necessary to Provide the Subcontract Works or
- supply Plant and Materials for the *subcontract works*.

(5) Trust Deed is an agreement in the form set out in the contract which contains provisions for administering the Project Bank Account.

(6) Joining Deed is an agreement in the form set out in the contract under which the Supplier joins the Trust Deed.

Named Suppliers Y1.2 The *Subcontractor* includes in his contracts with Subcontract Named Suppliers the arrangements in this contract for the operation of the Project Bank Account and Trust Deed. The *Subcontractor* notifies the Subcontract Named Suppliers of the details of the Project Bank Account and the arrangements for payment of amounts due under their contracts.

Y1.3 The *Subcontractor* submits proposals for adding a Supplier to the Subcontract Named Suppliers to the *Contractor* for acceptance. A reason for not accepting is that the addition of the Supplier does not comply with the Subcontract Works Information. The *Contractor,* the *Employer*, the *Subcontractor* and the Supplier sign the Joining Deed after acceptance.

Payments Y1.4 On or before each assessment date, the *Subcontractor* submits to the *Contractor* an application for payment, and shows in the application the amounts due to Subcontract Named Suppliers in accordance with their contracts.

Y1.5 The *Contractor* prepares the Authorisation, setting out the sums due to Subcontract Named Suppliers as assessed by the *Subcontractor* and to the *Subcontractor* for the balance of the payment due under the contract. The *Contractor* notifies the *Subcontractor* of the sums due to the *Subcontractor* and Subcontract Named Suppliers stated in the Authorisation.

Y1.6 The *Employer* and the *Contractor* make payment into the *project bank* of the amount stated in the Authorisation.

Y1.7 The *Subcontractor* and Subcontract Named Suppliers receive payment from the Project Bank Account of the sums set out in the Authorisation as soon as practicable after the Project Bank Account receives payment.

Y1.8 A payment which is due from the *Subcontractor* to the *Contractor* is not made through the Project Bank Account.

core clauses

main option clauses

secondary option clauses

cost components

subcontract data

Effect of payment Y1.9 Payments made from the Project Bank Account are treated as payments from the *Contractor* to the *Subcontractor* in accordance with this contract or from the *Subcontractor* or Subsubcontractor to Subcontract Named Suppliers in accordance with their contracts as applicable. A delay in payment due to a failure of the *Subcontractor* to comply with the requirements of this clause is not treated as late payment under this contract.

If the *Subcontractor* is identified as a Named Supplier in the Contract Data for the *Contractor*'s contract with the *Employer*

Trust Deed Y1.10 The *Employer*, the *Contractor*, the *Subcontractor* and *named suppliers* sign the Trust Deed before the first assessment date in the contract between the *Contractor* and the *Employer*.

If the *Subcontractor* is added as a Named Supplier after the Contract Date in the *Contractor*'s contract with the *Employer*

Trust Deed Y1.10 The *Employer*, the *Contractor*, the *Subcontractor* and the Named Supplier sign the Joining Deed before the first assessment date.

Termination Y1.11 If the *Contractor* issues a termination certificate, no further payment is made into the Project Bank Account.

Trust Deed

This agreement is made between the *Employer,* the *Contractor* and the Named Suppliers.

Terms in this deed have the meanings given to them in the contract between .... and .... for .... (the *works*).

Background

The *Employer* and the *Contractor* have entered into a contract for the *works.*

The Named Suppliers have entered into contracts with the *Contractor* or a Subcontractor in connection with the *works.*

The *Contractor* has established a Project Bank Account to make provision for payment to the *Contractor* and the Named Suppliers.

Agreement

The parties to this deed agree that

- sums due to the *Contractor* and Named Suppliers and set out in the Authorisation are held in trust in the Project Bank Account by the *Contractor* for distribution to the *Contractor* and Named Suppliers in accordance with the banking arrangements applicable to the Project Bank Account,
- further Named Suppliers may be added as parties to this deed with the agreement of the *Employer* and *Contractor.* The agreement of the *Employer* and *Contractor* is treated as agreement by the Named Suppliers who are parties to this deed,
- this deed is subject to the law of the contract for the *works,*
- the benefits under this deed may not be assigned.

Executed as a deed on ....

by

.... (*Employer*)

.... (*Contractor*)

....

....

....

....

(Named Suppliers)

Joining Deed

This agreement is made between the *Employer,* the *Contractor* and .... (the Additional Supplier).

Terms in this deed have the meanings given to them in the contract between .... and .... for .... (the *works*).

Background

The *Employer* and the *Contractor* have entered into a contract for the *works.*

The Named Suppliers have entered into contracts with the *Contractor* or a Subcontractor in connection with the *works.*

The *Contractor* has established a Project Bank Account to make provision for payment to the *Contractor* and the Named Suppliers.

The *Employer,* the *Contractor* and the Named Suppliers have entered into a deed as set out in Annex 1 (the Trust Deed), and have agreed that the Additional Supplier may join that deed.

Agreement

The Parties to this deed agree that

- the Additional Supplier becomes a party to the Trust Deed from the date set out below,
- this deed is subject to the law of the contract for the *works,*
- the benefits under this deed may not be assigned.

Executed as a deed on ....

by

.... (*Employer*)

.... (*Contractor*)

.... (Additional Supplier)

Option Y(UK)2: The Housing Grants, Construction and Regeneration Act 1996

Definitions   **Y(UK)2**

Y2.1   (1) The Act is the Housing Grants, Construction and Regeneration Act 1996 as amended by the Local Democracy, Economic Development and Construction Act 2009.

(2) A period of time stated in days is a period calculated in accordance with Section 116 of the Act.

Dates for payment   Y2.2   The date on which a payment becomes due is fourteen days after the assessment date.

The final date for payment is fourteen days or a different period for payment if stated in the Subcontract Data after the date on which payment becomes due.

The *Contractor*'s certificate is the notice of payment to the *Subcontractor* specifying the amount due at the payment due date (the notified sum) and stating the basis on which the amount was calculated.

Notice of intention   Y2.3   If either Party intends to pay less than the notified sum, he notifies the other
to pay less   Party not later than seven days (the prescribed period) before the final date for payment by stating the amount considered to be due and the basis on which that sum is calculated. A Party does not withhold payment of an amount due under this contract unless he has notified his intention to pay less than the notified sum as required by this subcontract.

Suspension of   Y2.4   If the *Subcontractor* exercises his right under the Act to suspend performance,
performance   it is a compensation event.

Option Y(UK)3: The Contracts (Rights of Third Parties) Act 1999

Third party rights   **Y(UK)3**

Y3.1   A person or organisation who is not one of the Parties may enforce a term of this subcontract under the Contracts (Rights of Third Parties) Act 1999 only if the term and the person or organisation are stated in the Subcontract Data.

Option Z: *Additional conditions of subcontract*

Additional conditions of   **Z1**
subcontract   Z1.1   The *additional conditions of subcontract* stated in the Subcontract Data are part of this subcontract.

Side tab: core clauses / main option clauses / secondary option clauses / cost components / subcontract data

SCHEDULE OF COST COMPONENTS

core clauses

main option clauses

secondary option clauses

cost components

subcontract data

This schedule is part of the *conditions of subcontract* only when Option C, D or E is used. In this schedule the *Subcontractor* means the *Subcontractor* and not his Subsubcontractors. An amount is included only in one cost component and only if it is incurred in order to Provide the Subcontract Works.

People 1 The following components of the cost of

- people who are directly employed by the *Subcontractor* and whose normal place of working is within the Working Areas and
- people who are directly employed by the *Subcontractor* and whose normal place of working is not within the Working Areas but who are working in the Working Areas.

11 Wages, salaries and amounts paid by the *Subcontractor* for people paid according to the time worked while they are within the Working Areas.

12 Payments to people for

(a) bonuses and incentives
(b) overtime
(c) working in special circumstances
(d) special allowances
(e) absence due to sickness and holidays
(f) severance related to work on this subcontract.

13 Payments made in relation to people for

(a) travel
(b) subsistence and lodging
(c) relocation
(d) medical examinations
(e) passports and visas
(f) travel insurance
(g) items (a) to (f) for dependants
(h) protective clothing
(i) meeting the requirements of the law
(j) pensions and life assurance
(k) death benefit
(l) occupational accident benefits
(m) medical aid
(n) a vehicle
(o) safety training.

14 The following components of the cost of people who are not directly employed by the *Subcontractor* but are paid for by him according to the time worked while they are within the Working Areas.

Amounts paid by the *Subcontractor*.

Equipment 2 The following components of the cost of Equipment which is used within the Working Areas (including the cost of accommodation but excluding Equipment cost covered by the percentage for Working Areas overheads).

21 Payments for the hire or rent of Equipment not owned by

- the *Subcontractor*,
- his parent company or
- by a company with the same parent company

at the hire or rental rate multiplied by the time for which the Equipment is required.

22   Payments for Equipment which is not listed in the Subcontract Data but is

- owned by the *Subcontractor*,
- purchased by the *Subcontractor* under a hire purchase or lease agreement or
- hired by the *Subcontractor* from the *Subcontractor*'s parent company or another part of a group with the same parent company

at open market rates multiplied by the time for which the Equipment is required.

23   Payments for Equipment purchased for work included in this subcontract listed with a time-related on cost charge, in the Subcontract Data, of

- the change in value over the period for which the Equipment is required and
- the time-related on cost charge stated in the Subcontract Data for the period for which the Equipment is required.

The change in value is the difference between the purchase price and either the sale price or the open market sale price at the end of the period for which the Equipment is required. Interim payments of the change in value are made at each assessment date. A final payment is made in the next assessment after the change in value has been determined.

If the *Contractor* agrees, an additional item of Equipment may be assessed as if it had been listed in the Subcontract Data.

24   Payments for special Equipment that is listed in the Subcontract Data. These amounts are the rates stated in the Subcontract Data multiplied by the time for which the Equipment is required.

If the *Contractor* agrees, an additional item of special Equipment may be assessed as if it had been listed in the Subcontract Data.

25   Payments for the purchase price of Equipment which is consumed.

26   Unless included in the hire or rental rates, payments for

- transporting Equipment to and from the Working Areas other than for repair and maintenance
- erecting and dismantling Equipment and
- constructing, fabricating or modifying Equipment as a result of a compensation event.

27   Payments for purchase of materials used to construct or fabricate Equipment.

28   Unless included in the hire rates, the cost of operatives is included in the cost of people.

Plant and Materials 3   The following components of the cost of Plant and Materials.

31   Payments for

- purchasing Plant and Materials,
- delivery to and removal from the Working Areas,
- providing and removing packaging and
- samples and tests.

32   Cost is credited with payments received for disposal of Plant and Materials unless the cost is disallowed.

Charges 4   The following components of the cost of charges paid by the *Subcontractor*.

41   Payments for provision and use in the Working Areas of

- water,
- gas and
- electricity.

core clauses

main option clauses

secondary option clauses

cost components

subcontract data

42 Payments to public authorities and other properly constituted authorities of charges which they are authorised to make in respect of the *subcontract works*.

43 Payments for

(a) cancellation charges arising from a compensation event
(b) buying or leasing land
(c) compensation for loss of crops or buildings
(d) royalties
(e) inspection certificates
(f) charges for access to the Working Areas
(g) facilities for visits to the Working Areas by Others
(h) specialist services
(i) consumables and equipment provided by the *Subcontractor* for the *Contractor*'s office.

44 A charge for overhead costs incurred within the Working Areas calculated by applying the percentage for Working Areas overheads stated in the Subcontract Data to the total of people items 11, 12, 13 and 14. The charge includes provision and use of equipment, supplies and services, but excludes accommodation, for

(a) catering
(b) medical facilities and first aid
(c) recreation
(d) sanitation
(e) security
(f) copying
(g) telephone, telex, fax, radio and CCTV
(h) surveying and setting out
(i) computing
(j) hand tools not powered by compressed air.

Manufacture and fabrication 5 The following components of the cost of manufacture and fabrication of Plant and Materials which are

• wholly or partly designed specifically for the *subcontract works* and
• manufactured or fabricated outside the Working Areas.

51 The total of the hours worked by employees multiplied by the hourly rates stated in the Subcontract Data for the categories of employees listed.

52 An amount for overheads calculated by multiplying this total by the percentage for manufacturing and fabrication overheads stated in the Subcontract Data.

Design 6 The following components of the cost of design of the *subcontract works* and Equipment done outside the Working Areas.

61 The total of the hours worked by employees multiplied by the hourly rates stated in the Subcontract Data for the categories of employees listed.

62 An amount for overheads calculated by multiplying this total by the percentage for design overheads stated in the Subcontract Data.

63 The cost of travel to and from the Working Areas for the categories of design employees listed in the Subcontract Data.

Insurance 7 The following are deducted from cost

• the cost of events for which this subcontract requires the *Subcontractor* to insure and
• other costs paid to the *Subcontractor* by insurers.

Sidebar tabs: core clauses | main option clauses | secondary option clauses | cost components | subcontract data

SHORTER SCHEDULE OF COST COMPONENTS

This schedule is part of the *conditions of subcontract* in all Options. When Option C, D or E is used, this schedule is used by agreement for assessing compensation events. When Option C, D or E is used, in this schedule the *Subcontractor* means the *Subcontractor* and not his Subsubcontractors. An amount is included only in one cost component and only if it is incurred in order to Provide the Subcontract Works.

People 1 The following components of the cost of

- people who are directly employed by the *Subcontractor* and whose normal place of working is within the Working Areas,
- people who are directly employed by the *Subcontractor* and whose normal place of working is not within the Working Areas but who are working in the Working Areas and
- people who are not directly employed by the *Subcontractor* but are paid for by him according to the time worked while they are within the Working Areas.

11 Amounts paid by the *Subcontractor* including those for meeting the requirements of the law and for pension provision.

Equipment 2 The following components of the cost of Equipment which is used within the Working Areas (including the cost of accommodation but excluding Equipment cost covered by the percentage for people overheads).

21 Amounts for Equipment which is in the published list stated in the Subcontract Data. These amounts are calculated by applying the percentage adjustment for listed Equipment stated in the Subcontract Data to the rates in the published list and by multiplying the resulting rate by the time for which the Equipment is required.

22 Amounts for Equipment listed in the Subcontract Data which is not in the published list stated in the Subcontract Data. These amounts are the rates stated in the Subcontract Data multiplied by the time for which the Equipment is required.

23 The time required is expressed in hours, days, weeks or months consistently with the list of items of Equipment in the Subcontract Data or with the published list stated in the Subcontract Data.

24 Unless the item is in the published list and the rate includes the cost component, payments for

- transporting Equipment to and from the Working Areas other than for repair and maintenance,
- erecting and dismantling Equipment and
- constructing, fabricating or modifying Equipment as a result of a compensation event.

25 Unless the item is in the published list and the rate includes the cost component, the purchase price of Equipment which is consumed.

26 Unless included in the rate in the published list, the cost of operatives is included in the cost of people.

© copyright nec 2013   61

	27	Amounts for Equipment which is neither in the published list, stated in the Subcontract Data nor listed in the Subcontract Data, at competitively tendered or open market rates, multiplied by the time for which the Equipment is required.
Plant and Materials	**3**	The following components of the cost of Plant and Materials.
	31	Payments for

- purchasing Plant and Materials,
- delivery to and removal from the Working Areas,
- providing and removing packaging and
- samples and tests.

	32	Cost is credited with payments received for disposal of Plant and Materials unless the cost is disallowed.
Charges	**4**	
	41	The following components of the cost of charges paid by the *Subcontractor*.

A charge calculated by applying the percentage for people overheads stated in the Subcontract Data to people item 11 to cover the costs of

- payments for the provision and use in the Working Areas of water, gas, and electricity,
- payments for buying or leasing land, compensation for loss of crops or buildings, royalties, inspection certificates, charges for access to the Working Areas and facilities for visits to the Working Areas by Others and
- payments for the provision and use of equipment, supplies and services (excluding accommodation) for catering, medical facilities and first aid, recreation, sanitation, security, copying, telephones, telex, fax, radio, CCTV, surveying, setting out, computing and hand tools not powered by compressed air.

	42	Payments for cancellation charges arising from a compensation event.
	43	Payments to public authorities and other properly constituted authorities of charges which they are authorised to make in respect of the *subcontract works*.
	44	Consumables and equipment provided by the *Subcontractor* for the *Contractor*'s office.
	45	Specialist services.
Manufacture and fabrication	**5**	The following components of the cost of manufacture and fabrication of Plant and Materials, which are

- wholly or partly designed specifically for the *subcontract works* and
- manufactured or fabricated outside the Working Areas.

	51	Amounts paid by the *Subcontractor*.
Design	**6**	The following components of the cost of design of the *subcontract works* and Equipment done outside the Working Areas.
	61	The total of the hours worked by employees multiplied by the hourly rates stated in the Subcontract Data for the categories of employees listed.
	62	An amount for overheads calculated by multiplying this total by the percentage for design overheads stated in the Subcontract Data.
	63	The cost of travel to and from the Working Areas for the categories of design employees listed in the Subcontract Data.
Insurance	**7**	The following are deducted from cost:

- costs against which this subcontract required the *Subcontractor* to insure and
- other costs paid to the *Subcontractor* by insurers.

SUBCONTRACT DATA

Part one – Data provided by the *Contractor*

Completion of the data in full, according to the Options chosen, is essential to create a complete subcontract.

Statements given in all subcontracts

1 General

- The *conditions of subcontract* are the core clauses and the clauses for main Option ....., dispute resolution Option ..... and secondary Options ..... of the NEC3 Engineering and Construction Subcontract April 2013.

- The *works* in the main contract are

  ....

- The *subcontract works* are

  ....

- The *Contractor* is

  Name ....

  Address ....

  ....

- The *Employer* in the main contract is

  Name ....

  Address ....

  ....

- The *Project Manager* in the main contract is

  Name ....

  Address ....

  ....

- The *Supervisor* in the main contract is

  Name ....

  Address ....

  ....

- The *Adjudicator* in this subcontract is

  Name ....

  Address ....

  ....

- The *main contract Adjudicator* is

  Name ....

  Address ....

  ....

- The Subcontract Works Information is in

  ....

  ....

  ....

- The Site Information is in

  ....

  ....

  ....

- The *boundaries of the site* are..................................

- The *language of this subcontract* is...............................

- The *law of the subcontract* is the law of ....

- The *period for reply* is

  for a reply by the *Contractor* .... weeks

  for a reply by the *Subcontractor* .... weeks.

- The *Adjudicator nominating body* is...............................

- The *tribunal* is ....

  ....

- The following matters will be included in the Risk Register

  ....

  ....

  ....

3 Time

- The *subcontract starting date* is ....

- The *subcontract access dates* are

Part of the Site	Date
1	....
2	....
3	....

- The *Subcontractor* submits revised programmes at intervals no longer than

  .... weeks.

4 Testing and Defects

- The *defects date* is .... weeks after Completion of the whole of the *subcontract works*.

- The *defect correction period* is .... weeks except that

  - The *defect correction period* for ....is .... weeks

  - The *defect correction period* for .... is .... weeks.

Sidebar tabs: core clauses | main option clauses | secondary option clauses | cost components | subcontract data

5 Payment

- The *currency of this subcontract* is the . . . .

- The *assessment interval* is . . . . weeks (not more than five).

- The *interest rate* is . . . .% per annum (not less than 2) above the . . . .
rate of the . . . . bank.

6 Compensation events

- The place where weather is to be recorded is

. . . .

- The *weather measurements* to be recorded for each calendar month are
  - the cumulative rainfall (mm)
  - the number of days with rainfall more than 5 mm
  - the number of days with minimum air temperature less than 0 degrees Celsius
  - the number of days with snow lying at . . . . hours GMT
  - and these measurements:

      . . . .

      . . . .

      . . . .

- The *weather measurements* are supplied by . . . .

- The *weather data* are the records of past *weather measurements* for each calendar month which were recorded at . . . .
and which are available from . . . .

. . . .

Where no recorded data are available

- Assumed values for the ten year return *weather data* for each *weather measurement* for each calendar month are

. . . .

. . . .

. . . .

. . . .

8 Risks and insurance

- The minimum limit of indemnity for insurance in respect of loss of or damage to property (except the *subcontract works*, Plant and Materials and Equipment) and liability for bodily injury to or death of a person (not an employee of the *Subcontractor*) caused by activity in connection with this subcontract for any one event is

. . . .

- The minimum limit of indemnity for insurance in respect of death of or bodily injury to employees of the *Subcontractor* arising out of and in the course of their employment in connection with this subcontract for any one event is

. . . .

core clauses

main option clauses

secondary option clauses

cost components

subcontract data

Optional statements

If the *tribunal* is arbitration

- The *arbitration procedure* is . . . .
- The place where the arbitration is to be held is

  . . . .
- The person or organisation who will choose an arbitrator
  - if the Parties cannot agree a choice or
  - if the *arbitration procedure* does not state who selects an arbitrator is

  . . . .

If the *Contractor* has decided the *subcontract completion date* for the whole of the *subcontract works*

- The *subcontract completion date* for the whole of the *subcontract works* is

  . . . .

If the *Contractor* is not willing to take over the *subcontract works* before the Subcontract Completion Date

- The *Contractor* is not willing to take over the *subcontract works* before the Subcontract Completion Date.

If no programme is identified in part two of the Subcontract Data

- The *Subcontractor* is to submit a first programme for acceptance within

  . . . . weeks of the Subcontract Date.

If the *Contractor* has identified work which is to meet a stated *condition* by a *key date*

- The *key dates* and *conditions* to be met are

condition to be met	*key date*
1	. . . .
2	. . . .
3	. . . .

If the period in which payments are made is not four weeks and Y(UK)2 is not used

- The period within which payments are made is . . . .

If Y(UK)2 is used and the final date for payment is not 14 days after the date when payment is due

- The period for payment is . . . .

If there are additional *Employer*'s or *Contractor*'s risks

- These are additional *Employer*'s risks

  1 . . . .

  2 . . . .

  3 . . . .

- These are additional *Contractor*'s risks

  1 . . . .

  2 . . . .

  3 . . . .

If the *Employer* or *Contractor* is to provide Plant and Materials

- The insurance against loss of or damage to the *subcontract works*, Plant and Materials is to include cover for Plant and Materials provided by the *Employer* or *Contractor* for an amount of

  . . . .

If the *Employer* or *Contractor* is to provide any of the insurances stated in the Insurance Table

- The *Employer* or *Contractor* provides these insurances from the Insurance Table

  1. Insurance against. . . . .

  Cover/indemnity is . . . .

  The deductibles are. . . . .

  2. Insurance against. . . . .

  Cover/indemnity is . . . .

  The deductibles are. . . . .

  3. Insurance against. . . . .

  Cover/indemnity is . . . .

  The deductibles are. . . . .

If additional insurances are to be provided

- The *Employer* or *Contractor* provides these additional insurances

  1. Insurance against. . . . .

  Cover/indemnity is . . . .

  The deductibles are. . . . .

  2. Insurance against. . . . .

  Cover/indemnity is . . . .

  The deductibles are. . . . .

  3. Insurance against. . . . .

  Cover/indemnity is . . . .

  The deductibles are. . . . .

core clauses

main option clauses

secondary option clauses

cost components

subcontract data

- The *Subcontractor* provides these additional insurances

    1. Insurance against. . . . .

    Cover/indemnity is . . . .

    2. Insurance against. . . . .

    Cover/indemnity is . . . .

    3. Insurance against. . . . .

    Cover/indemnity is . . . .

If Option B or D is used

- The *method of measurement* is . . . .

    amended as follows . . . .

    . . . .

    . . . .

If Option C or D is used

- The *Subcontractor*'s *share percentages* and the *share ranges* are

share range	Subcontractor's share percentage
less than . . . . %	. . . . %
from . . . . % to . . . . %	. . . . %
from . . . . % to . . . . %	. . . . %
greater than . . . . %	. . . . %.

If Option C, D or E is used

- The *Subcontractor* prepares forecasts of Defined Cost for the *subcontract works* at intervals no longer than . . . . weeks.

- The *exchange rates* are those published in. . . . .

    on . . . . (date).

If Option X1 is used

- The proportions used to calculate the Price Adjustment Factor are

    0. . . . . linked to the index for . . . .

    0. . . . .

    0. . . . .

    0. . . . .

    0. . . . .

    0. . . . .

    0. . . . . non-adjustable

    _____

    1.00

- The *base date* for indices is . . . .

- The indices are those prepared by. . . . .

core clauses

main option clauses

secondary option clauses

cost components

subcontract data

If Option X3 is used

- The *Contractor* will pay for the items or activities listed below in the currencies stated

items and activities	other currency	total maximum payment in the currency
. . . .	. . . .	. . . .
. . . .	. . . .	. . . .
. . . .	. . . .	. . . .
. . . .	. . . .	. . . .

- The *exchange rates* are those published in . . . .

  on . . . . (date).

If Option X5 is used

- The *subcontract completion date* for each *section* of the *subcontract works* is

section	description	subcontract completion date
1	. . . .	. . . .
2	. . . .	. . . .
3	. . . .	. . . .
4	. . . .	. . . .

If Options X5 and X6 are used together

- The bonus for each *section* of the *subcontract works* is

section	description	amount per day
1	. . . .	. . . .
2	. . . .	. . . .
3	. . . .	. . . .
4	. . . .	. . . .

  Remainder of the *subcontract works* . . . .

If Options X5 and X7 are used together

- Delay damages for each *section* of the *subcontract works* are

section	description	amount per day
1	. . . .	. . . .
2	. . . .	. . . .
3	. . . .	. . . .
4	. . . .	. . . .

  Remainder of the *subcontract works* . . . .

If Option X6 is used (but not if Option X5 is also used)

- The bonus for the whole of the *subcontract works* is . . . . per day.

core clauses

main option clauses

secondary option clauses

cost components

subcontract data

If Option X7 is used (but not if Option X5 is also used)

- Delay damages for Completion of the whole of the *subcontract works* are
  . . . . per day.

If Option X12 is used

- The *Client* is

  Name . . . .

  Address . . . .

  . . . .

- The *Client*'s *objective* is

  . . . .

  . . . .

  . . . .

  . . . .

  . . . .

  . . . .

- The Partnering Information is in

  . . . .

  . . . .

  . . . .

  . . . .

If Option X13 is used

- The amount of the performance bond is . . . .

If Option X14 is used

- The amount of the advanced payment is . . . .
- The *Subcontractor* repays the instalments in assessments starting not less
  than . . . . weeks after the Subcontract Date.
- The instalments are . . . .

  . . . .

  (either an amount or a percentage of the payment otherwise due)

- An advanced payment bond <u>is/is not</u> required.

If Option X16 is used

- The *retention free amount* is . . . .
- The *retention percentage* is . . . . %.

If Option X17 is used

- The amounts for low performance damages are

  amount   performance level

  . . . .   for . . . .

  . . . .   for . . . .

  . . . .   for . . . .

  . . . .   for . . . .

If Option X18 is used

- The *Subcontractor*'s liability to the *Contractor* for indirect or consequential loss is limited to . . . .

- For any one event, the *Subcontractor*'s liability to the *Contractor* for loss of or damage to the *Employer*'s or *Contractor*'s property is limited to . . . .

- The *Subcontractor*'s liability for Defects due to his design which are not listed on the Defects Certificate is limited to . . . .

- The *Subcontractor*'s total liability to the *Contractor* for all matters arising under or in connection with this subcontract, other than the excluded matters, is limited to . . . .

- The *end of liability date* is . . . . years after the Completion of the whole of the *subcontract works*.

If Option X20 is used (but not if Option X12 is also used)

- The *incentive schedule* for Key Performance Indicators is in . . . .

- A report of performance against each Key Performance Indicator is provided at intervals of . . . . months.

If Option Y(UK)3 is used

- term   person or organisation

  . . . .

  . . . .

  . . . .

  . . . .

If Options Y(UK)1 and Y(UK)3 are both used

- term   person or organisation

  The provisions of Option Y(UK)1   Subcontract Named Suppliers

If Option Z is used

- The *additional conditions of subcontract* are . . . .

  . . . .

core clauses

main option clauses

secondary option clauses

cost components

subcontract data

Part two – Data provided by the *Subcontractor*

Completion of the data in full, according to the Options chosen, is essential to create a complete subcontract.

- The *Subcontractor* is

  Name ....

  Address ....

  ....

- The *direct fee percentage* is .... %.
- The *subsubcontracted fee percentage* is. .... %.
- The *subcontract working areas* are the Site and ....
- The key people are

  (1) Name. ....

  Job ....

  Responsibilities. ....

  ....

  Qualifications ....

  Experience. ....

  ....

  (2) Name. ....

  Job ....

  Responsibilities. ....

  ....

  Qualifications. ....

  Experience. ....

  ....

- The following matters will be included in the Risk Register

  ....

  ....

  ....

  ....

core clauses

main option clauses

secondary option clauses

cost components

subcontract data

Optional statements

If the *Subcontractor* is to provide Subcontract Works Information for his design

- The Subcontract Works Information for the *Subcontractor*'s design is in

  ....

  ....

  ....

  ....

  ....

If a programme is to be identified in the Subcontract Data

- The programme identified in the Subcontract Data is ....

If the *Subcontractor* is to decide the *completion date* for the whole of the *subcontract works*

- The *subcontract completion date* for the whole of the *subcontract works* is ....

If Option A or C is used

- The *activity schedule* is ....

If Option B or D is used

- The *bill of quantities* is...

If Option A, B, C or D is used

- The tendered total of the Prices is ....

If Option Y(UK)1 is used

- *named suppliers* are ....

If Option A or B is used

Data for the Shorter Schedule of Cost Components

- The percentage for people overheads is...........................%.
- The published list of Equipment is the last edition of the list published by ....
- The percentage for adjustment for Equipment in the published list is .... % (state plus or minus).
- The rates for other Equipment are

Equipment	size or capacity	rate
....	....	....
....	....	....
....	....	....
....	....	....

- The hourly rates for Defined Cost of design outside the Working Areas are

category of employee	hourly rate
....	....
....	....
....	....
....	....

core clauses

main option clauses

secondary option clauses

cost components

subcontract data

- The percentage for design overheads is. . . . . %.
- The categories of design employees whose travelling expenses to and from the Working Areas are included in Defined Cost are

. . . .

. . . .

. . . .

. . . .

If Option C, D or E is used

Data for Schedule of Cost Components

- The listed items of Equipment purchased for work on this subcontract, with an on cost charge, are

Equipment	time-related charge	per time period
. . . .	. . . .	per . . . .
. . . .	. . . .	per . . . .
. . . .	. . . .	per . . . .
. . . .	. . . .	per . . . .

- The rates for special Equipment are

Equipment	size or capacity	rate
. . . .	. . . .	. . . .
. . . .	. . . .	. . . .
. . . .	. . . .	. . . .
. . . .	. . . .	. . . .

- The percentage for Working Areas overheads is . . . . %.
- The hourly rates for Defined Cost of manufacture and fabrication outside the Working Areas are

category of employee	hourly rate
. . . .	. . . .
. . . .	. . . .
. . . .	. . . .
. . . .	. . . .

- The percentage for manufacture and fabrication overheads is . . . . %.

If Option C, D or E is used

Data for both schedules of cost components

- The hourly rates for Defined Cost of design outside the Working Areas are

category of employee	hourly rate
. . . .	. . . .
. . . .	. . . .
. . . .	. . . .
. . . .	. . . .

- The percentage for design overheads is. . . . . %.

core clauses

main option clauses

secondary option clauses

cost components

subcontract data

- The categories of design employees whose travelling expenses to and from the Working Areas are included as a cost of design of the *subcontract works* and Equipment done outside of the Working Areas are

....

....

....

....

If Option C, D or E is used

Data for the Shorter Schedule of Cost Components

- The percentage for people overheads is...........................%.
- The published list of Equipment is the last edition of the list published by

....

- The percentage for adjustment for Equipment in the published list is

.... % (state plus or minus).

- The rates for other Equipment are

Equipment	size or capacity	rate
....	....	....
....	....	....
....	....	....
....	....	....

core clauses

main option clauses

secondary option clauses

cost components

subcontract data

nec®3 Engineering and Construction Subcontract

Index by clause numbers (Option clauses are indicated by their letters, main clause heads by bold numbers). Terms in *italics* are identified in Subcontract Data, and defined terms have capital initial letters.

acceleration **36**, 60.1(9), A36.3, B36.3, C36.3, D36.3, E36.4
acceptance
  addition to Working Areas 15.1
  conditions of subcontract 26.3
  contract data for subsubcontract C26.4, D26.4, E26.4
  Defects **44**, 60.1(1)(9)
  Equipment design 23.1
  form of communication 13.1
  insurance policies/certificates 85.1, 87.1, 87.2
  procedure C11.2(25), D11.2(25), E11.2(25)
  programme (first/revised) 31.3, 32.2, 50.3, 64.1–2, A31.4, A36.3, B36.3, C31.4, C36.3, D36.3
  quotations 44.2, 60.1(9), 62.3, 65.1, A36.3, B36.3, C36.3, D36.3, E36.4
  reasons for withholding 13.4, 13.8, 15.1, 21.2, 23.1, 24.1, 26.2–3, 31.3, 60.1(9), 85.1, 87.1, A54.3, C26.4, D26.4, E26.4, X13.1
  replacement *Subcontractor*'s employee 24.1
  subcontract conditions 26.3
  Subcontractor's communication 13.4, 13.8, 14.1
  Subcontractor's design 21.2, 21.3
  Subsubcontractor 26.2, 91.2
Accepted Programme
  absence 64.2
  and Activity Schedule A54.2, A54.3, C54.2, C54.3
  changes 32.1, 63.7
  Contract Date 60.1(19)
  dates/times 33.1, 60.1(2)(3)(5), 63.3
  definition 11.2(1)
  Key Dates 63.3
  prevention 19.1, 60.1(19)
  termination 91.7
  see also programme
access 27.2, 31.2, 33.1, 43.4, 45.1–2, 60.1(2)
access date 30.1, 31.2, 33.1, 60.1(2)
accounts and records, *Subcontractor*'s C11.2(25), C52.2–3, D11.2(25), D52.2–3, E11.2(25), E52.2–3
actions **10**, 11.2(13)(14), 14.2, 16.3
Activity Schedule A11.2(20), A31.4, A54.1–A54.3, A63.12, C11.2(20), C31.4, C54.1–C54.3, C63.12
  revised A54.2–3, C54.2–3
Acts
  Contracts (Rights of Third Parties) (1999) **Y(UK)3**
  Housing Grants, Construction and Regeneration (1996) as amended by the Local Democracy, Economic Development and Construction Act 2009 **W1, W2, Y(UK)2**
additional conditions of subcontract **Z1**
additional costs 25.3

address for communications 13.2
adjudication W1.3, W2.3
  timings W1.3(8–11), W2.3(2)(8)(11–12)
Adjudication Table W1.3(1)
Adjudicator
  appointment W2.2(1)
  decisions 51.3
  dispute resolution W1.1–3, W2.2(1–5)
  nominating body W1.2(3), W2.2(3)
  not arbitrator W1.2(2), W2.2(2)
  payment certificates 51.3
  replacement W1.2(4), W2.2(4)
  resignation W1.2(3), W2.2(3), W2.3(1)
  reviews/revisions W2.3(4)
  tribunal W1.3(2)(10), W2.3(11)
  tribunal reviews W1.4, W2.4(1–3)
administration order 91.1
advanced payment 93.1, **X14**
  repayment X14.3
advanced payment bond X14.2
agents of *Adjudicator* W1.2(5), W2.2(5)
agreement, *law of the subcontract* 12.4
ambiguities **17**, 60.3, 63.8, B60.6, D60.6
amount due
  adjustment for inflation X1.1(b), X1.2, X1.4, X1.5
  and advanced payment repayment 93.1, X14.3
  assessing **50**, 51.1, 51.3, 90.4, 93.1, C50.6, C53.3–4, D50.6, D53.7–8, E50.7, X1.4
  correction of assessment 50.5, 51.3, X1.2
  definition 50.2
  payment 51.1, 51.3
  retention in 93.1
  on termination 90.2, 90.4, 93.1, 93.2, A93.3
amount retained 50.3, X16.1, X16.2
applicable law 11.2(5), 21.2, 23.1, 40.1, 84.2
approval from Others 27.1–2
arbitration procedure W1.4(5), W2.4(4)
arrangement with creditors 91.1
assessment
  Adjudicator W1.3(7), W2.3(7)
  amount due **50**, 51.1, 51.3, 90.4, 93.1, C50.6, C53.3, C53.4, D50.6, D53.7, D53.8, E50.7, X1.1(b), X1.2, X1.4, X1.5
  compensation events 60.1(12), 62.2–3, **63, 64**, 65.1–2, **A63.**, A65.4, B63.10–13, C52.2, C63.11–12, C63.15, D52.2, **D63**, E52.2, E63.15, X1.3
  Defect(s) correction cost 45.1–2
  interest 51.2, 51.3
  Subcontractor's share C53.1, C53.3–4, C93.4, C93.6, D53.5, D53.7–8, D93.5–6
  tests/inspections cost 40.6
assessment date 50.1, 50.4, 51.1–2
assessment interval 50.1

assignment of benefit 92.2
Authorisation
    Project Bank Account Y1.1(1), Y1.5, Y1.6
availability of resources C11.2(25), D11.2(25),
    E11.2(25)

bank bonds X13.1, X14.2
bankruptcy 91.1
base date X1.1(a), X1.3
Base Date Index X1.1(a)
bill of quantities B11.2(21), D11.2(21)
Bill of Quantities B11.2(21)(28)(31), B55.1,
    B60.4–B60.7, B63.13, D11.2(21)(31)(33),
    D55.1, D60.4–D60.7, D63.13
bodily injury 84.2
bond(s) 91.2, X13.1, X14.2
bonus for early Completion **X6**
boundaries of the site 11.2(15)
breach of contract 60.1(18)
breach of statutory duty 80.1

calculation(s)
    assessment of compensation events for
        Subsubcontractors C52.2, D52.2, E52.2
    Fee 11.2(8), 63.1, 93.2, C50.6, D50.6, E50.7
certificate(s)/certification
    communication of 13.1, 13.6
    Completion 30.2, 35.2
    Defects 43.3, 50.1
    insurance 85.1, 87.1–3
    payment 50.5, 51.1, 51.2, 90.4, 91.4
    take-over date 35.3, 60.1(15)
    termination 90.1, 90.3–4, C93.4, D93.5
changed Completion Date X7.2
changed decision(s) 60.1(8), 61.1, 61.2–3
change(s) in Activity Schedule A54.2, A63.12, C54.2,
    C63.12
change(s) in *conditions of subcontract* 12.3
change(s) in forecast Prices and Subcontract
    Completion Date due to compensation events
    E65.3
change(s) in Key Dates due to compensation events
    D60.6, D65.4
change(s) in the law **X2**
change(s) of Prices
    departure from *method of measurement* B60.6,
        D60.6
    due to compensation events B63.10, B63.13,
        C63.12, D65.4
    and Subcontract Completion Date due to
        compensation events 62.2, 63.1, 63.8,
        A63.12, A65.4, B65.4, C65.4, D63.11,
        D63.13, D65.4
change(s) in Subcontract Works Information 14.3,
    18.1, 44.1, 44.2, 60.1(1), 63.2, 63.8
civil commotion, risks due to 80.1
claims
    Contractor's risks 80.1
    Employer's risks 80.1
    indemnity against 83.1–3
co-operation and mutual trust 10.1, 26.3
co-operation with Others 25.1

communications **13**
    and acceptance of submission 13.4, 13.8, 14.1
    address to which sent 13.2
    Adjudicator W1.3(6), W2.3(6)
    assessment of compensation events for
        Subsubcontractors C52.2, D52.2, E52.2
    certificate(s) 13.6
    form defined 13.1
    notification(s) 13.7
    period for reply 13.3, 13.5
    time allowed for reply 13.3, 13.5, 31.3, 32.2,
        60.1(6)
    time when effective 13.2
compensation
    Contractor's and *Employer*'s risks 80.1
    see also indemnity
compensation events **60**
    amount due affected by 51.3
    assessing 60.1(12), 62.2–3, **63**, **64**, 65.1–2,
        A63.10, A63.12, A63.14, B63.10, B63.13,
        C52.2, C63.11–12, C63.15, D52.2, **D63**,
        E63.15, X1.3
    assumptions made 60.1(17), 61.6, 63.2, 63.8,
        65.2
    Completion Date not affected by 61.4
    Contractor's assessments **64**, A63.10, A63.14,
        B63.10, B63.13, C63.11, C63.15, D63.15,
        E63.15
    Contractor's rights 63.4
    definitions 13.8, 60.1, B60.4–7, D60.4–7, X2.1,
        X14.2
    implementing 32.1, **65**, A65.4, B65.4, C65.4,
        D65.4, E65.3
    Key Dates 62.2, 63.3, A65.4, D65.4
    notifying **61**, X2.1
    payment to Subsubcontractor C11.2(25)
    performance suspension Y2.4
    Prices affected by 62.2, 63.1, A63.12, A65.4,
        B60.6, B63.10, B63.13, B65.4, C65.4, D60.6,
        D63.11, D63.13, D65.4, X2.1
    Prices not affected by 61.4
    quotations 61.4–5, **62**, 63.1, 64.1, 64.3–4, 65.1,
        A11.2(22), B11.2(22), X2.1
    records of assessment E52.2
    Risk Register 16.1
    risks 63.6
    Subcontract Completion Date affected by 62.2,
        A65.4, B65.4, C65.4, D65.4
    Subcontractor 60.1(1)(8)(10)(12)(19), 60.2,
        60.3, 65.1
    Subcontractor's fault 61.4
    Subcontractor's rights 63.4
    time allowed 61.1, 61.3, 61.4, 64.3, 64.4
completed activity, definition A11.2(27)
completed work B11.2(28)
    definition D11.2(33)
Completion **30**
    acceleration of 36.1
    bonus paid if early X6.1
    certification 30.2, 35.2
    and compensation events 61.4, B60.5, D60.5
    decision on date 30.2

Completion (*continued*)
  definition 11.2(2)
  early warning of possible delay 16.1
  and notification of Defects 43.2
  and programme 31.2, 32.2
  section of the *subcontract works* X5.1
  and take over of *subcontract works* 35.1–2,
    60.1(15), X16.1, X16.2
  whole of *subcontract works* 32.2, 50.1, 60.1(13),
    92.1, 93.2, C20.4, C53.3, D20.4, D53.7,
    E20.4, X1.2, X16.1
  work necessary 11.2(2)(13)
Completion Date
  change to later date X7.2
  see also Subcontract Completion Date
Condition 11.2(9)
conditions of subcontract
  additional Z1.1
  changes 12.3
  identified and defined terms 11.1
  and sectional Completion X5.1
Construction and Regeneration Act (1996) as
    amended by the Local Democracy, Economic
    Development and Construction Act 2009 **W1**, **W2**,
    Y(UK)2
Contract Date
  Accepted Programme 60.1(19)
  compensation events 60.1(19)
  termination 91.7
Contractor
  acceleration 36.1, A36.3, B36.3, C36.3, D36.3,
    E36.4
  acceptance of communication/proposal/submission
    13.4, 14.1, 15.1, 21.2, 31.3, 85.1
  acceptance of contract data for subsubcontract
    C26.4, D26.4, E26.4
  acceptance of quotation 44.2, 60.1(9), 62.3,
    62.6, 65.1, A36.3, B36.3, C36.3, D36.3,
    E36.4
  access 27.2, 33.1, 43.4, 60.1(2)
  Activity Schedule A54.2, C54.2
  addition to *working areas* 15.1
  adjudication W1.3(1–11), W2.3(3)(4)
  Adjudicator's reviews/revisions W1.3(5)
  advanced payment X14.3
  ambiguities 17.1
  amount due to be paid by 50.2, 51.1
  assessment of amount due 50.1, 50.4, 50.5
  assessment of compensation events 61.6, **64**,
    A63.10, A63.14, B63.10, B63.13, C63.11,
    C63.14, C63.15, D63.11, D63.13, D63.15,
    E63.14, E63.15, F63.14
  assessment date decided by 50.1
  assessment of Defect(s) correction cost
    45.1–2
  assessment of *Subcontractor*'s share C53.1, C53.3,
    C53.4, C93.4, C93.6, D53.5, D53.7, D53.8,
    D93.5, D93.6
  assessment of test/inspection cost 40.6
  assumptions about compensation events 60.1(17),
    61.6, 63.2
  breach of contract by 60.1(18)

certificates 13.6, 30.2, 50.5, 51.1, 51.3,
    60.1(15), 82.1, 90.1, 90.3–4, C93.4, D93.5
co-operation 10.1, 25.1
compensation events 60.1(1–11)(14–18), 63.4,
    A63.10, A63.14, B63.10, B63.13, C63.11,
    C63.15, C65.4, D63.15, E63.15
Completion 30.2
completion of *subcontract works* on termination
    93.1, 93.2
correction of mistakes in Bill of Quantities B60.6,
    D60.6
date of Completion 30.2
dates 31.2, 33.1, 60.1(2–3)(5)
decisions 30.2, 60.1(8), 61.1–2, 61.4–6,
    D11.2(25), E11.2(25)
defaults 91.6
Defect(s) acceptance/uncorrected 44.1–2
Defect(s) notified by 11.2(6)
Defect(s): rights 43.3
delegation 14.2
Disallowed Cost decision C11.2(25), D11.2(25),
    E11.2(25)
duties 10.1, **14**
early warning 16.1–2, 16.4, 61.5, 63.5
Equipment 23.1, 31.2, 71.1, 72.1
fault 80.1
forecasts of Defined Cost C20.4, D20.4, E20.4
hindered by *Subcontractor* 91.3
illegal/impossible requirements 18.1
implementing compensation events 65.1, B65.4,
    C65.4, E65.3
inconsistencies 17.1
indemnity 83.1
inspection of *Subcontractor*'s accounts and records
    C52.2, C52.3, D52.3, E52.3
instruction(s) 14.3, 17.1, 18.1, 24.2, 27.3, 34.1,
    36.1, 44.2, 60.1(1)(4)(7), 61.1–2, 61.4,
    62.1, 62.3–4, 82.1, 87.1, 91.6, C26.4,
    D26.4, E26.4, X2.1
insurance 84.1, 85.1, 85.3, 85.4, 86.1, **87**
interest on payments 51.3
Key Date 60.1(4)
marking of Equipment, Plant and Materials 71.1
moving of Equipment, Plant and Materials 72.1
moving of Plant and Materials 70.2
notification of
    compensation events 61.1, 61.3–6, X2.1
    implementing compensation events C65.4,
    E65.3
    Subcontractor's default 91.2, 91.3
objects of value/historical interest 60.1(7), 73.1
obligations 91.2
as Party to contract 11.2(11)
payment(s) 51.1
performance bond X13.1
performance indicators X20.3
Plant and Materials 31.2, 70.2, 71.1, 72.1, 80.1
prevention 19.1
programme 11.2(1), 31.1–3, 32.2, 50.3, 60.1(5)
Project Bank Account **Y(UK)1**
quotations for acceleration 36.1, 60.1(9), A36.3,
    B36.3, C36.3, D36.3

quotations for compensation events 62.1, 62.3–6
repayment of delay damages X7.2
reply to communication 13.3–5, 60.1(6), 62.3,
    62.5
request to remove resources from Working Areas
    C11.2(25), D11.2(25), E11.2(25)
responsibilities 83.2–3, 87.2
risks 60.1(14), **80**, 81.1, 83.2–3, 85.4
starting/stopping work 34.1, 60.1(4), 91.6
Subcontract Works Information 14.3, 18.1, 22.1,
    44.2, 60.1(1)(5)(16)
Subcontractor's advice C20.3, D20.3, E20.3
Subcontractor's default 91.2, 91.3
Subcontractor's design 11.2(5), 21.2, 22.1
Subcontractor's employees 24.1, 24.2
Subcontractor's parent company guarantee X4.1
subsubcontract conditions 26.3
Subsubcontractor acceptance 26.2, 91.2
take over of *subcontract works* 35.1–3, 43.4,
    60.1(15), 80.1, X6.1, X7.3, X16.1–2
termination 80.1, 90.1–4, 91.2–4, 92.1–2, 93.1–2
test materials/facilities/samples provided by 40.2,
    40.6, 60.1(16)
title to Plant and Materials **70**, 93.1
use of *subcontract works* 11.2(2)
Contractor's design 80.1
Contracts (Rights of Third Parties) Act (1999) **Y(UK)3**
Core Group, Partnering X12.1–3
correcting
    assessing compensation events D63.11
    assessment of amount due 50.5, 51.3, X1.2
    assumptions about compensation events 60.1(17),
        61.6, 63.2
    Bill of Quantities mistakes B60.6, D60.6, D60.7
    Defects 11.2(2), 32.1, 40.4, **43**, 45.1–2,
        C11.2(25), D11.2(23)(25), E11.2(25)
cost allowances 63.6
cost components data A11.2(22), B11.2(28),
    C11.2(23), C63.15, D11.2(23), D63.15,
    E11.2(23), E63.15
costs
    additional costs 25.3
    Contractor's risk 80.1
    Defect(s) correction 45.1–2
    due to *Adjudicator*'s/*tribunal*'s decision 51.3
    due to *tribunal*'s decision 51.3
    Employer's risk 80.1
    indemnity against 83.1, 83.2–3
    insurance 86.1, 87.3
    test/inspection repeat 40.6
creditors, arrangement made with 91.1
currency of this subcontract 51.1, C50.6, D50.6,
    E50.7, X3.1–2

damage(s)
    Contractor's risk 80.1
    delay X7.1, X7.2
    Employer's risk 80.1
    insurance against 84.2
    low performance X17.1
    repair by *Subcontractor* 82.1
death insurance 84.2

decision(s)
    Adjudicator or *tribunal* 51.3
    assessment date 50.1
    and compensation events 60.1(8), 61.1, 61.4–6
    Contractor 30.2, 50.1, 60.1(8), 61.1–2, 61.4–6,
        C11.2(25), D11.2(25), E11.2(25)
    date of Completion 30.2
    risk reduction meeting 16.4
defaults
    Contractor's 91.6
    Subcontractor's 91.2–3, 91.6
defect correction period 40.5, 43.2–4, 45.1
Defect(s)
    accepting **44**, 60.1(1)(9)
    correcting 11.2(2), 32.1, 40.4, **43**, 45.1–2,
        C11.2(25), D11.2(23)(25), E11.2(25)
    definition 11.2(5)
    liability limitation X18.3
    loss, damage or wear 80.1
    low performance damages X17.1
    notifying 11.2(6), 42.2, 43.1
    and priced contract(s) A11.2(27), B11.2(28)
    searching (for) 42.1, 60.1(10)
    Subcontractor's compensation X15.2
    Subcontractor's liability 11.2(5), X15.1, **X18**
    and tests/inspections 40.4, 40.6
    uncorrected **45**, 60.1(9)
Defects after Completion, Disallowed Cost D11.2(25)
Defects Certificate 43.3
    and assessment of amount due 50.1
    and *Contractor*'s risks 80.1
    correcting Defects 43.3
    definition 11.2(6)
    and insurance cover 84.2
    liability limitation X18.3
    low performance damages X17.1
    performance indicators X20.2
    and retention X16.2
    and *Subcontractor*'s risks 81.1
defects date 11.2(6), 40.5, 42.1–2, 43.3
    compensation events 61.7
Defined Cost **52**, E11.2(29)(32)
    in amount due on termination 93.1, 93.2
    calculation percentages 52.1
    and compensation events 61.4, 63.1, 63.2, 63.7,
        A63.10, B60.4, B63.10, B63.13, D60.4,
        D63.11, D63.13, X1.3, X2.1
    definition(s) A11.2(22), B11.2(22), C11.2(23),
        D11.2(23), E11.2(23)
    and Fee calculation 11.2(8), 63.1, C11.2(29),
        D11.2(29), E11.2(29)
    forecast C20.4, D20.4, E20.4
    inspection of records E52.3
    payment on termination C93.4, D93.5
    payments made by *Subcontractor* C50.6, C52.2,
        D50.6, D52.2, D52.3, E50.7, E52.2
    reduction due to compensation C63.11
defined terms **11**
Delay/delay
    and compensation events 62.2, 63.3, B60.5, D60.5
    damages X7.1, X7.2
    early warning to be given 16.1

Delay/delay (*continued*)*
  Key Dates 63.3
  plans to deal with 32.1
  and priced contract(s) A11.2(27), B11.2(28)
  and tests/inspections 40.5, 60.1(11)
delegation by *Contractor* 14.2
delivery
  Plant and Materials 41.1, 93.1
  testing and inspection before **41**
demolition 22.1, 73.2
design
  Contractor's 80.1
  Employer's 80.1
  Subcontract Equipment **23**
  subcontract works C20.3, D20.3, E20.3
  Subcontractor's 11.2(5), 21.2, 21.3, 22.1, 23.1,
    27.1
direct fee percentage 11.2(8), 93.2
Disallowed Cost C11.2(23), D11.2(23), E11.2(23)
  definition(s) C11.2(25), D11.2(25), E11.2(25)
discounts, deduction from prices 52.1
dismantling (during searching) 42.1
dispute resolution
  unless United Kingdom Housing Grants,
    Construction and Regeneration Act (1996) as
    amended by the Local Democracy, Economic
    Development and Construction Act 2009
    applies **W1**
  when United Kingdom Housing Grants, Construction
    and Regeneration Act (1996) as amended by
    the Local Democracy, Economic Development
    and Construction Act 2009 applies **W2**

early Completion bonus X6.1
early warning **16**
  effects 16.1
  responsibility 16.1, 61.5, 63.5, C11.2(25),
    D11.2(25), E11.2(25)
  Risk Register 11.2(14)
Effect of payment
  Project Bank Account Y1.9
employees
  Adjudicator's W1.2(5), W2.2(5)
  Subcontractor's 24.1, 24.2, 84.2
Employer
  Defects Certificate 43.3
  fault 80.1
  hindered by *Subcontractor* 91.3
  indemnity 83.1
  insurance 84.1, **87**
  programme 31.2, 60.1(5)
  Project Bank Account Y1.3, Y1.6, Y1.10
  responsibilities 87.2
  risks 60.1(14), **80**, 81.1, 83.2, 85.4
  Subcontract Works Information 60.1(5)
  tests and inspections 40.2, 60.1(16)
  use of *subcontract works* 11.2(2), 35.2
Employer's design 80.1
Equipment
  damage to 80.1, 84.2
  definition 11.2(7)
  design of **23**

left on Site 72.1, 80.1
loss of 80.1, 84.2
marking of 71.1
and programme 31.2
rates in Subcontract Data X1.3
removal of **72**, 92.2, 93.2
title 92.2
use by *Contractor* 92.2
errors, *Adjudicator* W1.3(11)
excavation materials 73.2
exchange rates C50.6, D50.6, E50.7, X3.1
experienced contractor
  and compensation events 60.1(12), 60.2, 61.5,
    63.5
  and physical conditions on Site 60.1(12), 60.2
extension of time for decision/quotation/reply 13.5,
    62.5

facilities and services, for tests/inspections 40.2,
    42.1, 60.1(16)
failure to pay in time, actions to be taken 91.4
fault of
  Contractor or his design 80.1
  Employer or his design 80.1
  Subcontractor 61.1, 61.4
Fee C11.2(29), D11.2(29), E11.2(29)(32)
  calculation(s) 11.2(8), 63.1, 93.2, C50.6, D50.6,
    E50.7
  Defined Cost 52.1
fee percentage see direct fee percentage
final decision, *Adjudicator* W1.3(10), W2.3(11)
float, provision in programme 31.2
forecasts 61.6, 63.1, 65.2, 93.2, C20.4, C53.3,
    D20.4, D53.7, E20.4, E65.3
fraud, and insurance 85.2

grouping of activities A11.2(27), A93.3
guarantee(s) 91.2, X4.1

health and safety
  regulation(s) 91.3
  requirements 31.2
  Subcontract Works Information 27.4
  Subcontractor 27.4
historical-interest objects found within Site 60.1(7),
    73.1
Housing Grants, Construction and Regeneration Act
    (1996) as amended by the Local Democracy,
    Economic Development and Construction Act
    2009 **W1**, **W2**, **Y(UK)2**

identified terms **11**
illegal requirements **18**
implementing compensation events 32.1, **65**, A65.4,
    B65.4, C65.4, D65.4, E65.3
impossible requirements **18**
incentive schedule X20.1
Incentive Schedule X20.1, X20.3–5
inconsistencies **17**, 60.3, 63.8, B60.6–7, D60.6–7
indemnity **83**
information
  in Activity Schedule A54.1, C54.1

in Bill of Quantities B55.1, D55.1
later recorded 65.2
in programme 31.2, 31.3, 50.3
provided to Others 25.1
publicly available 60.2
see also Site Information; Subcontract Works
    Information
injury insurance 84.2
inspection(s) **40**, 60.1(10)(11)
    before delivery **41**
    costs for repeats E40.7
instalment repayment of advanced payment X14.3
instruction(s)
    Adjudicator's W2.3(4–5)
    compensation events resulting 60.1(1)(4)(7), 61.1
    to *Contractor* 27.3
    form of communication 13.1
    insurance 87.1
    objects of value/interest 60.1(7)
    quotation(s) to be submitted 36.1, 61.1–2,
        61.5–6, 62.1, 62.3–4, 63.1, 64.1, X2.1
    to remove *Subcontractor*'s employee 24.2
    to search (for Defects) 42.1
    stopping/not starting work **34**, 60.1(4), 91.6
    to *Subcontractor* 27.3
    and termination 91.6, 92.2
    that change Subcontract Works Information 14.3,
        16.4, 18.1, 44.2, 60.1(1), 63.8
insurance
    certificates 85.1, 86.1, 87.1–3
    by *Contractor* 84.1, 85.4, 86.1, **87**
    cover **84**
    by *Employer* 84.1, 85.4, **87**
    insurer(s) 85.2, 85.4
    policies **85**, 86.1, 87.1–3
Insurance Table 84.2
insurer(s) X13.1, X14.2
insurrection risks 80.1
interest
    assessment of 51.2, 51.3
    calculation 51.4
    on late payment 51.2
    and payment certificate(s) 51.3
    repaid delay damages X7.2
interpretation
    compensation event 63.8
    legal **12**

Joining Deed
    Project Bank Account Y1.1(2), Y1.1(6), Y1.10

Key Date
    acceleration 36.1, B36.3, E36.4
    Accepted Programme 63.3
    change(s) in Subcontract Works Information 63.8–9
    co-operation 25.3
    and compensation events 60.1(4), 61.4, 62.2,
        63.3, A65.4, B60.5, B65.4, D60.5, D65.4,
        E65.3
    conditions of contract 25.3
    conditions of subcontract 30.3
    Contractor: compensation events 60.1(4)

Contractor: instructions 14.3
    definition 11.2(9)
    Delay/delay 63.3
    failing to meet D11.2(23)
    implementing compensation events C65.4
    and programme 31.2
    working with Others 25.3
Key Performance Indicators X12.4, **X20**
key person 24.1

language of this subcontract 13.1
late payment(s) 51.2, X14.2
later recorded information 65.2
Latest Index X1.1(b)
law
    changes in **X2**
    and Defect(s) 11.2(5)
    national legislation **Y**
    tests and inspections 40.1
law of the subcontract 12.2
legal rights, interference with 80.1
legislation, national **Y**
liability
    and insurance 84.2
    limitation **X18**
    reduction 83.2–3
    Subcontractor's design 14.1, X15.1
liquidator for company/partnership 91.1
loss risks 80.1, 84.2
low performance
    damages **X17**
    early warning of possibility 16.1
lump sum(s) A11.2(30), A63.14, B11.2(28)(31),
        B63.13, C11.2(30), C63.14, C93.5,
        D11.2(31)(33), D63.13, E63.14

marking of Equipment, Plant and Materials **71**
materials
    access to 27.2
    dates when needed 31.2
    testing/inspection before delivery 41.1
    for tests/inspections 40.2, 42.1, 60.1(16)
    title to 73.2
    see also Plant and Materials
method of measurement B60.6, D60.6
method of working 35.2, A54.2, C54.2
military power, risks due to 80.1
mistake(s)
    assessment of amount due 51.3
    Bill of Quantities B60.6, B60.7, D60.6, D60.7
multiple currencies **X3**
mutual trust and co-operation 10.1, 26.3

named person 24.1
named suppliers
    Project Bank Account Y1.1(2), Y1.10
Named Suppliers
    Project Bank Account Y1.2, Y1.3, Y1.10
national legislation **Y**
NEC contract 26.3, C26.4, D26.4, E26.4
negligence 80.1
nominating body, Adjudicator W1.2(3), W2.2(3)

notification
    acceptance of quotation(s) 62.3, 62.6, 65.1
    adjudication W1.3(1–2)(8–11), W2.3(1–2)(8–9)
    ambiguities/inconsistencies 17.1
    assessment of compensation event 62.3, 64.3–4,
        65.1
    communication of 13.1, 13.7
    compensation events and assumptions 60.1(17),
        61
    Contractor's assessment 64.3–4, 65.1
    Contractor's decision(s) 63.5, 64.1
    Defects 11.2(6), 42.2, 43.1
    delegate for *Contractor* 14.2
    early warning matters 11.2(14), 16.1
    illegal/impossible requirements 18.1
    implementing compensation events A65.4, B65.4,
        C65.4, D65.4, E65.3
    proposed instruction/changed-decision 61.2,
        62.3
    Risk Register 11.2(14)
    Subcontractor's default 91.2–3
    termination 90.1
    tests and inspections 40.3, 41.1
notified Defects, correction 32.1, 43.1, 45.1–2

objects of value or historical interest 60.1(7), 73.1
observing tests 40.3
operations (in programme) 31.2, 32.1
Others (other people)
    approval by 27.1–2
    at risk reduction meeting 16.2
    co-operation with 25.1
    Defect(s) correction by 45.1–2
    definition 11.2(10)
    hindered by *Subcontractor* 91.3
    Plant and Materials supplied by 80.1
    and programme 31.2, 60.1(5)
    Subcontract Works Information 60.1(5)
    working with 25.1, 25.3

parent company guarantee **X4**
Parties/Party
    Adjudicator's communications W1.3(6), W2.3(6)
    Adjudicator's instructions W1.3(5), W2.3(5)
    to contract 11.2(11)
    and determination 91.5
    indemnity liability 83.1–3
    insurance 84.2, 85.3
    law of the subcontract 12.4
    prevention 19.1
    Subcontract Works Information 63.8
    and termination 90.1, 91.1
    third party rights Y3.1
    tribunal reviews W1.4, W2.4(1–3)(5)
Partnering **X12**
    defined terms X12.1
    early warning X12.3(3)
    incentives X12.4
    Information/information X12.3(1-6)(8)
    Key Performance Indicators X12.4(1–2)
    subsubcontracting X12.3(9)
    timetable X12.3(7)

Partners
    actions X12.2
    Core Group X12.2(3–5)
    representatives X12.2(2)
payment(s) **51**
    advanced 93.1, X14.1–3
    certified 50.5, 51.1–2, 90.4
    conditional on success of test or inspection 40.5
    Contractor's insurance 87.3
    dates Y2.2
    Housing Grants, Construction and Regeneration Act
        (1996) as amended by the Local Democracy,
        Economic Development and Construction Act
        2009 Y2.2–3
    late 51.2, X14.2
    and marking of Equipment, Plant and Materials
        71.1
    not made 91.4
    notice of intention Y2.3
    Project Bank Account Y1.4, Y1.5, Y1.6, Y1.7, Y1.8,
        Y1.9
    Subcontractor 40.6, 45.1–2, 51.1, 86.1, C50.6,
        C52.2, D50.6, D52.2, E50.7, E52.2, X3.1–2,
        X14
    on termination **93**, A93.3, C93.4, C93.5–6, **D93**
    time to be made 51.2, X14.2
    withholding Y2.3
payment certificate 50.5, 51.1, 51.3, 91.4
payment clauses **50**
people **24**
    rates in Subcontract Data X1.3
    see also employees; Others
percentages
    Defined Cost 52.1
    see also direct fee percentage; retention percentage
performance bond **X13**
performance impairment
    early warning of possibility 16.1
    see also low performance
performance indicators see Key Performance
    Indicators
performance reports X20.2
performance suspension Y2.4
period for reply 13.3–5, 32.2, 36.2
personal injury 84.2
physical conditions of Site 60.1(12), 60.2, 60.3
Plant and Materials
    access to 27.2
    dates when needed 31.2
    definition 11.2(12)
    loss of or damage to 80.1, 82.1, 84.2
    marking of 70.1
    not used to Provide the Subcontract Works
        C11.2(25), D11.2(25), E11.2(25)
    removal of 92.2
    replacement 82.1, 84.2
    supply 11.2(17)
    and termination 92.1, 93.1
    testing/inspection before delivery 41.1
    title 70.1–2, 92.1, 93.1
    wastage C11.2(25), D11.2(25), E11.2(25)
prevention **19**

Price Adjustment Factor(s) **X1**
  assessment of compensation events X1.3
  calculation of X1.2
  definition X1.1(c)
  price adjustment use X1.4–5
Price for Work Done to Date
  adjustment for inflation X1.4–5
  and assessment of amount due 50.2–3, 93.2,
    C93.4, C93.6, D93.5
  and assessment of *Subcontractor*'s share C53.1–4,
    D53.5–8
  definition(s) A11.2(27), B11.2(28), C11.2(29),
    D11.2(29), E11.2(29)
  and retention X16.1
Prices/prices
  and acceleration 36.1, A36.3, B36.3, C36.3,
    D36.3
  and Activity Schedule A11.2(27)(30), A54.3,
    A63.12, C11.2(30), C54.3, C63.12
  and Bill of Quantities B11.2(31), B60.4, B60.6,
    B63.13, D11.2(31)(33), D60.4, D60.6, D63.13
  and change to Subcontract Works Information
    B63.10
  and compensation events 61.4, 62.2, 63.1–2,
    A63.10, A63.12, A65.4, B60.4, B60.6,
    B63.10, B63.13, B65.4, C63.11–12, C63.14,
    C65.4, D60.4, D60.6, D63.11, D63.13,
    D65.4, E63.14, E65.3, X2.1
  competitively tendered/open market 52.1
  definition E11.2(32)
  early warning of possible increase 16.1
  if Defect(s) uncorrected/accepted 44.2
  reduction A63.10
  Subcontractor's share C53.1–4, D53.5–8
  and termination 93.2, C93.4–6, D93.5
procedures
  acceptance C11.2(25), D11.2(25), E11.2(25)
  arbitration procedure W1.4(5), W2.4(4)
  procurement C11.2(25), D11.2(25), E11.2(25)
  termination 90.2–3, **92**
proceedings
  Contractor's and *Employer*'s risk 80.1
  indemnity against 83.1–3
procurement procedure C11.2(25), D11.2(25),
    E11.2(25)
programme 11.2(1), **31**, 50.3, 62.2, 64.1
  acceleration 36.1, A36.3, B36.3, C36.3, D36.3,
    E36.4
  dates to be shown 31.2, 32.1, A31.4, C31.4
  revised **32**, 36.1, 62.2, 64.2, A36.3, B36.3, C36.3,
    D36.3, E36.4
  see also Accepted Programme
Project Bank Account **Y(UK)1**
Project Manager, access for 27.2
property, loss or damage 84.2
proposal(s)
  acceleration 36.1
  to add to Working Areas 15.1
  Defect(s) acceptance/uncorrected 44.1
  form of communication 13.1
  risk reduction meeting 16.3
proposed instruction or changed decision 61.2, 62.3

Provide the Subcontract Works **20**
  and addition to Working Areas 15.1
  after termination 90.5
  and Equipment 11.2(7), 23.1
  meaning of term 11.2(13)
  Plant and Materials not used C11.2(25),
    D11.2(25), E11.2(25)
  and programme 31.2
  resources not used C11.2(25), D11.2(25),
    E11.2(25)
  and Subcontract Works Information 11.2(19), 20.1,
    C11.2(25), D11.2(25), E11.2(25)
  Subcontractor's responsibilities 11.2(7), 14.1,
    20.1, 23.1, 26.2–3, C20.4, C26.4, D20.3,
    D26.4, E20.3–4, E26.4
publicly available information 60.2

quantities *see* Bill of Quantities
quotations
  for acceleration 36.1–2, 60.1(9), A36.3, B36.3,
    C36.3, D36.3, E36.4
  acceptance of 36.1, 44.2, 60.1(9), 62.3, 62.6,
    65.1, A36.3, B36.3, C36.3, D36.3
  for compensation events 61.4–5, **62**, 63.1, 64.1,
    64.3–4, 65.1, A11.2(22), B11.2(22), X2.1
  if Defect(s) accepted 44.2, 60.1(9)
  for proposed instruction/changed decision 61.2
  revised 62.3–4, 64.1

radioactive contamination 80.1
rates
  in assessment of compensation events A63.14
  in Bill of Quantities B11.2(28)(31), B60.4,
    B63.13, D11.2(31), D60.4, D63.13
  in Subcontract Data X1.3, X6.1, X7.1
rebates, deduction from prices 52.1
rebellion, risks due to 80.1
receiver over assets 91.1
records
  assessment of compensation events for
    Subsubcontractors E52.2
  form of communication 13.1
  risk reduction meeting 16.4
  Subcontractor's C11.2(25), C52.2–3, D11.2(25),
    D52.2–3, E11.2(25), E52.2–3
re-covering (during searching) 42.1
re-erecting (during searching) 42.1
referral, adjudication W1.3(1–3), W2.3(1–3)
registered risk 16.1, 16.3–4
removing
  Equipment **72**, 92.2, 93.2
  of items from Risk Register 16.4
  Plant and Materials 92.2
  resources C11.2(25), D11.2(25), E11.2(25)
  Subcontractor's employee 24.2
repairs **82**
replacement(s)
  of *Adjudicator* W1.2(4), W2.2(4)
  Plant and Materials 80.1, 82.1, 84.2
  Subcontractor's employee 24.1
reply
  form of communication 13.1

reply (*continued*)
  time allowed 13.3–5, 31.3, 32.2, 36.2, 60.1(6), 62.5–6
resignation of *Adjudicator* W1.2(3), W2.2(3), W2.3(1)
resources
  identified in operation statement 31.2
  not used to Provide the Subcontract Works C11.2(25), D11.2(25), E11.2(25)
responsibilities
  Contractor's 83.2–3, 87.2
  Employer's 87.2
  Subcontractor's 11.2(7), 14.1, **20–7**, 83.2
retention 50.3, 93.1, **X16**
retention free amount X16.1
retention percentage X16.1
reviews, *tribunal* W1.4(1–6), W2.4(1–5)
revised Activity Schedule A54.2–3, C54.2–3
revised programme **32**, 36.1, 62.2, 64.2, A36.3, B36.3, C36.3, D36.3, E36.4
revised quotation 62.3–4, 64.1
revolution, risks due to 80.1
Rights of Third Parties (Contracts) Act 1999 **Y(UK)3**
riots, risks due to 80.1
risk reduction meeting
  purpose 16.3
  records 16.4
  who attends 16.2
Risk Register
  compensation events 16.1
  definition 11.2(14)
  entering early warning issues 16.1
  removal of items 16.4
risks
  compensation events 63.6
  Contractor's 60.1(14), **80**, 81.1, 83.2–3, 85.4
  description 11.2(14)
  Employer's 60.1(14), **80**, 81.1, 83.2, 85.4
  Subcontractor's 63.6, **81**, 84.2, 85.4

safety *see* health and safety
samples 40.2, 42.1, 60.1(16)
Schedule of Cost Components A11.2(22), D11.2(23), E11.2(23)
  Shorter Schedule B11.2(22), C63.15, D63.15, E63.15
Schedule of Partners X12.1–4
searching for Defects 42.1, 60.1(10)
section of the *subcontract works* X5.1
sectional Completion **X5**
services 11.2(13)
  see also facilities and services
share ranges C53.1, D53.5
Shorter Schedule of Cost Components B11.2(22), C63.15, D63.15, E63.15
Site
  access to 31.2, 33.1, 60.1(2)
  definition 11.2(15)
  historical-interest/valuable objects found 60.1(7), 73.1
  information describing 11.2(16)
  location X2.1
  physical conditions 60.1(12), 60.2–3

removal of Equipment, Plant and Materials 72.1, 92.2
  and risks 80.1
  starting of work 30.1
  visual inspection 60.2
Site Information 11.2(16), 60.2–3
  and Activity Schedule A54.1, C54.1
  and Bill of Quantities B55.1, D55.1
start(ing) work 30.1
  instruction(s) given not to 34.1, 60.1(4), 91.6
  see also subcontract starting date
statement, operations (in programme) 31.2
stopping work 34.1, 60.1(4), 91.6
strikes, risks due to 80.1
subcontract access date 30.1, 31.2, 33.1, 60.1(2)
Subcontract Completion Date (*subcontract completion date*)
  acceleration 36.1, A36.3, B36.3, C36.3, D36.3, E36.4
  and compensation events 60.1(13)(15), 61.4, 62.2, 63.3, A65.4, B65.4, C65.4, D65.4, E65.3
  definition 11.2(3)
  if Defect(s) accepted 44.2
  Price Adjustment Factor calculation X1.2
  in programme (first/revised) 31.2, 36.1, A36.3, B36.3, C36.3, D36.3
  section of the *subcontract works* X5.1
  and take over of *subcontract works* 35.1, 60.1(15)
  and *weather measurement* 60.1(13)
  work to be done by 11.2(2), 30.1
Subcontract Data/subcontract data
  addresses 13.2
  Adjudicator identified W1.2(3), W2.2(3)
  Condition 11.2(9)
  conditions of subcontract Z1.1
  Contractor's and *Employer*'s risks 80.1
  currencies for payment X3.1–2
  delay damages X7.1
  documents referred to in 11.2(16)(19)
  early Completion bonus X6.1
  forecasts of Defined Cost C20.4, D20.4, E20.4
  insurance 84.1, 87.2
  low performance damages X17.1
  named key person 24.1
  payment period 51.2
  performance bond X13.1
  performance level X17.1
  price adjustment for inflation X1.1(c), X1.3
  programme 11.2(1), 31.1, 50.3
  Risk Register 11.2(14)
  start-to-Completion interval 32.2
  for subsubcontract C26.4, D26.4, E26.4
  take over of *subcontract works* 35.1
  terms identified 11.1
  third party rights Y3.1
  weather data/weather measurement 60.1(13)
Subcontract Date 11.2(4), 60.1(12), B60.4, D60.4, X4.1, X13.1, X14.1–3
Subcontract Named Suppliers
  Project Bank Account Y1.1(1), Y1.1(2), Y(1.1(3), Y1.2, Y1.3, Y1.4, Y1.5, Y1.7, Y1.9

subcontract starting date 31.2, 32.2, 50.1, 81.1, 84.2, 85.1, 87.1, C20.4, D20.4, E20.4
dispute resolution W1.2(1), W2.2(1)
subcontract works
completion of whole 32.2, 50.1, 60.1(13), 92.1, 93.2, C20.4, C53.3–4, D20.4, D53.7, E20.4, X1.2, X16.1
and Defects 11.2(5)
design C20.3, D20.3, E20.3
early warning of possible performance impairment 16.1
Equipment left in 72.1
information specifying/describing 11.2(19), 25.1
loss of or damage to 80.1, 82.1, 84.2
Plant and Materials included 11.2(12)(17)
section X5.1
Subcontractor's design 21.1, 22.1, X15.1
and Subsubcontractor 11.2(17)
taking over **35**, 43.4, 60.1(15), 80.1, X6.1, X7.3, X16.1–2
wear to 80.1
work necessary to complete 11.2(13), 92.1
Subcontract Works Information
acceptance/procurement procedure C11.2(25), D11.2(25), E11.2(25)
and Activity Schedule A54.1, C54.1
advanced payment bond X14.2
assessing compensation events D63.11
assessment of compensation A63.10
and Bill of Quantities B55.1, D55.1
change(s) 14.3, 18.1, 44.1–2, 60.1(1), 63.8, A63.10
and compensation events 60.1(1)(16), 63.8, B63.10, C63.11
conditions not stated in 60.1(5)
conditions stated in 25.1, 60.1(5)
and Defects 44.1–2
Defined Cost reduction A63.10
definition 11.2(19)
early warning of changes 16.4
Equipment 11.2(7)
health and safety 27.4
instructions that change 14.3, 16.4, 18.1, 44.2, 60.1(1), 63.8
Key Date change(s) 63.8–9
marking of Equipment, Plant and Materials 71.1
performance bond X13.1
and programme 31.2
Project Bank Account Y1.3
and Providing the Subcontract Works 20.1, C11.2(25), D11.2(25), E11.2(25)
Subcontract Completion Date 11.2(2)
Subcontractor's accounts and records C52.2–3, D52.2, E52.2
Subcontractor's design 21.1–2, 22.1, 60.1(1), X15.1
Subcontractor's parent company guarantee X4.1
take over of *subcontract works* 35.2
tests and inspections 40.1–2, 41.1, 42.1, 60.1(16)
title to materials 73.2
uncorrected Defects 45.1

Subcontractor
acceleration 36.1–2
acceptance of communication/proposal/submission 13.4, 13.8, 14.1, 15.1, 21.2, 87.2
access 27.2, 33.1, 43.4
accounts and records C11.2(25), C52.2–3, D11.2(25), D52.2–3, E11.2(25), E52.2–3
Activity Schedule A31.4, A54.2, C31.4, C54.2
adding to *working areas* 15.1
adjudication W1.3(1–11), W2.3(3)(7)
advanced payment by X14.1–3
advice to *Contractor* C20.3, D20.3, E20.3
ambiguities/inconsistencies 17.1
amount due to be paid to 50.2, 50.4, 51.1
assessment of compensation events 62.2, 64.1, B63.13, C52.2, C63.11, C63.15, D52.2, D63.11, D63.13, D63.15, E63.15
Bill of Quantities B11.2(28), B63.13, D63.13
certificates issued to 13.6
co-operation 25.1
compensation assessment records E52.2
compensation events 60.1(1)(8)(10)(12)(19), 60.2–3, 63.4
assessments 62.2, 64.1, B63.13, C52.2, C63.11, C63.15, D52.2, D63.11, D63.13, D63.15, E63.15
implementation 32.1, 65.1, E65.3
costs 52.1
decisions communicated to 30.2, 60.1(8)
defaults 91.2–3, 91.6
Defect(s) 42.2
Defect(s) acceptance/uncorrected 44.1–2
Defect(s) correction 43.1–2, 43.4, 45.1–2, C11.2(25), D11.2(25), E11.2(25)
delay damages X7.1
delivery of Plant and Materials 41.1, 93.1
duties 10.1
early Completion bonus X6.1
early warning 16.1, 16.2, 16.4, 61.5, 63.5
Equipment 11.2(7), 23.1, 31.2, 92.2
fault 61.1, 61.4, D11.2(25), E11.2(25)
health and safety 27.4
illegal/impossible requirements 18.1
implementing compensation events 32.1, 65.1, E65.3
inconsistencies with Bill of Quantities B60.7
instructions 14.3, 24.2, 27.3, 34.1, 36.1, 60.1(10), 61.2, 61.4–6, 62.1, 62.3–4, 82.1, 87.1, 91.6, C26.4, D26.4, E26.4
insurance 84.1–2, 85.1, 85.3–4, 86.1, 87.1–3
leaving of Site/Working Areas 92.2
liabilities 14.1, 61.4, X15.1
liability limitation **X18**
low-performance damages X17.1
marking of Equipment, Plant and Materials 71.1
method of working 35.2, A54.2, C54.2
notification of compensation events 61.1, 61.3–4
notified of delegate for *Contractor* 14.2
objects of value/historical-interest 73.1
obligations 91.2
parent company guarantee X4.1
as Party to contract 11.2(11)

Subcontractor (*continued*)
  payment(s) 40.6, 45.1–2, 51.1, 86.1, B63.13,
    C50.6, C52.2, D50.6, D52.2, E50.7, E52.2,
    X3.1–2
  performance bond X13.1
  period for reply 13.3–5, 32.2
  physical conditions 60.1(12), 60.2–3
  Plant and Materials 27.2, 41.1, 80.1, 92.2, 93.1
  programme (first/revised) 11.2(1), 31.1–3,
    32.1–2, 50.3, 62.2, 64.1–2
  Project Bank Account **Y(UK)1**
  proposed instruction/changed-decision 61.2
  quotations 36.1–2, 44.2, 62.1–5, 64.1
  rates and lump sums A63.14
  reaction to compensation event 63.7
  repairs/replacements 82.1
  reply to communication 13.3–5, 31.3, 32.2,
    60.1(6), 62.3–6
  responsibilities 14.1, **20–7**, 83.2, C20.3–4, C26.4,
    D20.3–4, D26.4, E20.3–4, E26.4
  risks 63.6, **81**, 84.2, 85.4
  starting/stopping work 30.1, 34.1, 91.6
  subcontract contract data C26.4
  Subcontract Works Information 11.2(19), 14.3, 63.8
  subsubcontract contract data D26.4, E26.4
  subsubcontracted work C20.3, D20.3, E20.3
  Subsubcontractor 11.2(17), 26.1–2
  take over of *subcontract works* 43.4, 80.1
  termination 80.1, 90.1–2, 90.4–5, 91.2
  test materials/facilities/samples provided by 40.2,
    40.3, 40.5–6, 41.1, 60.1(16)
  title to objects and materials within Site 73.1–2
  title to Plant and Materials 70.1–2
  uncorrected Defects 45.1–2
Subcontractor's design **21**
  approval from Others 27.1
  and Defects 11.2(5)
  and Equipment design 23.1
  liability of *Subcontractor* 14.1, X15.1
  limitation of *Subcontractor*'s liability X15.1
  part submission 21.3
  and Subcontract Works Information 21.1–2, 60.1(1)
  submission to *Contractor* 21.2
  use by *Contractor* and *Employer* 22.1
Subcontractor's employees 24.1
  insurance 84.2
  removing 24.2
Subcontractor's share C50.6, **C53**, C93.4, C93.6,
  D50.6, **D53**, D93.5–6
Subcontractor's *share percentage* C53.1, D53.5
submission(s)
  addition to Working Areas 15.1
  communications 13.1, 13.4
  Equipment design 23.1
  forecasts of total Defined Cost C20.4, D20.4, E20.4
  insurance policies/certificates 85.1, 86.1, 87.1,
    87.3
  non-acceptance of 13.8, 15.1, 21.2, 23.1, 26.2–3
  programme (first/revised) 31.2, 32.2, 50.3,
    64.1–2, A31.4, C31.4
  quotations 36.1–2, 44.2, 61.4, 62.1, 62.3–6,
    63.1, 64.1, X2.1

Subcontractor/subcontract conditions/contract
  data C26.4
Subcontractor's design 21.2
Subsubcontractor/subcontract conditions/contract
  data D26.4, E26.4
Subsubcontractor/subsubcontract conditions 26.2,
  26.3
subrogation rights 85.2
subsubcontract
  adjudication W1.3(4)
  assignment of benefits 92.2
  conditions 26.3
  contract data C26.4, D26.4, E26.4
subsubcontracted work, Defined Cost A11.2(22),
  B11.2(22), C11.2(23), D11.2(23), E11.2(23)
subsubcontracting **26**, C20.3, C26.4, D20.3, D26.4,
  E20.3, E26.4
Subsubcontractor
  acceptance by *Contractor* 26.2, 91.2
  appointment 26.2–3, 91.2
  definition 11.2(17)
  payment(s) C11.2(23)(25), D11.2(23)(25),
    E11.2(23)
Supervisor
  access for 27.2
  tests and inspections 40.3, 40.5, 42.1, 60.1(11)
suppliers 11.2(17)
  Project Bank Account Y1.1(2), Y1.1(4), Y1.1(6),
    Y1.3

take over of *subcontract works* **35**, 43.4, 60.1(15),
  80.1, X6.1, X7.3, X16.1–2
taxes 50.2, 52.1
termination **90**
  amount due on 90.2, 90.4, 93.1–2, A93.3
  certification of 90.1, 90.3, C93.4, D93.5
  loss/damage risks 80.1
  payment on **93**, A93.3, C93.4, C93.6, D93.5–6
  procedures 90.2–3, **92**
  Project Bank Account Y1.11
  Providing the Subcontract Works 90.5
  reasons 90.2, **91**
Termination Table 90.2, 92.2, 93.2
tests/testing **40**, 42.1
  before delivery **41**
  compensation events resulting 60.1(10)(11)(16)
  costs for repeats E40.7
third party rights, Contracts Act Y3.1
time allowed
  certification of Completion 30.2
  certification of payment 50.5, 51.1, 90.4
  certification of take over 35.3
  compensation events 61.1, 61.3–4, 64.3–4
  extension(s) agreed 13.5, 62.5
  payment of amount due 51.2, 91.4
  programme submission/acceptance 31.1, 31.3,
    32.2
  reply to communications 13.3, 13.5, 31.3, 32.2,
    36.2, 60.1(6), 62.5–6
  start/restart of work 91.6
time clauses **30**
time risk allowances 31.2, 63.6

title
    Equipment, Plant and Materials 92.2
    materials from excavation and demolition 73.2
    object of value or historical interest 73.1
    Plant and Materials **70**, 92.1–2
total of the Prices
    adjustment for inflation X1.5
    early warning of possible increase 16.1
    payment on termination 93.2, C93.4, D93.5
tribunal
    Adjudicator W1.3(2)(10), W2.3(11)
    arbitration W1.4(5), W2.4(4)
    costs 51.3
    decisions 51.3
    Disallowed Cost D11.2(25), E11.2(25)
    payment certificates 51.3
    reviews W1.4(1–6), W2.4(1–5)
Trust Deed
    Project Bank Account Y1.1(6), Y1.1(5), Y1.2, Y1.10

uncorrected Defects **45**, 60.1(9)
uncovering (during search) 42.1
undecided disputes, *Adjudicator* W1.2(4), W2.2(4)
United Kingdom Housing Grants, Construction and
    Regeneration Act (1996) as amended by the
    Local Democracy, Economic Development and
    Construction Act 2009 **W1**, **W2**, **Y(UK)2**
use of *subcontract works* by *Contractor/Employer*
    11.2(2), 35.2
usurped power, risks due to 80.1
utilisation of resources C11.2(25), D11.2(25),
    E11.2(25)

valuable objects found within Site 60.1(7), 73.1
visual inspection of Site 60.2

waiver by insurers 85.2
war 80.1
wastage of Plant and Materials C11.2(25),
    D11.2(25), E11.2(25)
watching tests 40.3
wear, risks due to 80.1
weather conditions 60.1(12)
weather data/weather measurement 60.1(13)
whole of the *subcontract works* X5.1
    Completion 32.2, 50.1, 60.1(13), 92.1, 93.2,
        C20.4, C53.3–4, D20.4, D53.7, E20.4, X1.2,
        X16.1
    Defined Cost C20.4, D20.4, E20.4
winding-up order 91.1
witnesses, *tribunal* proceedings W1.4(6), W2.4(5)
Working Areas (*working areas*) 11.2(18)
    addition **15**
    Equipment, Plant and Materials outside 71.1
    Equipment, Plant and Materials removed from 92.2
    Equipment, Plant and Materials within 41.1
    Plant and Materials outside 70.1, 70.2, 71.1
    Plant and Materials within 41.1, 70.2, 93.1
    resources removed from C11.2(25),
        D11.2(23)(25), E11.2(25)
    sharing with Others 25.1
working with *Contractor*/Others **25**
Works Information *see* Subcontract Works Information